W9-BSM-588

What readers are saying...

"Fast read, very entertaining, this story made me realize how much more I could be enjoying my work and my life."
Rebecca Herwick
President and CEO
Global Products, Inc

"Great is the only word to describe this book. Easy-to-read, interesting and exciting, it is a great way to learn about a tough subject. Get this book!"
Bill Brooks, Best Selling Author
The New Science of Selling and Persuasion

"During my career I have read hundreds of books that all claimed to help people grow personally and professionally. This book is one of the few that delivers solid ideas and motivation to help anyone. I highly recommend it to anyone who is interested in personal and career development."

Tim Connor, Best selling author
Soft Sell, 81 Management Challenges and Above Ground

Riding the Waves Without Getting Wet

"A loveable character, and another that finds himself. A cool story that packs a punch. Surprise and philosophy. All packed in a novelette that is so worth the read. Give yourself the gift of this wise book."
John P. Schuster
Author, *Answering Your Call*, coach for coaches, grandfather, Businessman

"A parable for leaders or those who aspire to be, Riding the Waves forces you to reflect on what kind of person you are or want to be and that choice is within all of us."
Richard (Rick) D. Amme
Media & Crisis Consultant
Amme & Associates, Inc.

"Who would have thought a book about leadership and relationships could be so absorbing, so much fun to read and have some great principles, too! I simply couldn't put it down."
Jerry V. Teplitz, JD, Ph.D., CSP
Author, Brain Gym For Business, Managing Your Stress and Switched-On Living

Riding the Waves Without Getting Wet

A Leadership Parable

Riding the Waves Without Getting Wet

A Leadership Parable

Mike Hourigan and Kathleen Smith

Catawba Publishing
Charlotte, NC

Special discounts on bulk quantities of Riding the Waves Without Getting Wet® books are available to corporations, professional associations, other organizations and learning institutions. For details, contact:
Ride The Waves Group, LLC., Sales Department, PO Box 860525, Shawnee, KS 860525
Tel.: 913.422.9000 Fax: 913.422.9096

Website: www.ridethewaves.com

Library of Congress Cataloguing-in-Publication Data

Hourigan, Mike, and Smith, Kathleen.
Riding the waves without getting wet: a leadership parable / Mike Hourigan and Kathleen Smith.
p. cm.
Includes bibliographical references. ISBN 978-0-9672917-4-1 (paperback)
1. Leadership. 2. Executive ability. 3. Ethics. 4. Values. 5. Change. I. Title
HD00.0.000000 2007
658.4'0'000—00dc00 2007000000

Illustrations by Bob Bliss

Cover Design by Meghan O'Leary

Catawba Publishing www.catawba.com

DEDICATIONS

To my wife, Debbie. You provided not only a compass but also the lighthouse. Your support and encouragement were the beacon and sometimes the foghorn necessary for me to complete this project.

Mike

To my daughter, Jennifer, without whom the waves I have ridden would not have been so worthwhile. You have always been my North Star, the magnetic force in my compass, my best reason to weather any storm and head back to shore.

Kathleen

ACKNOWLEDGEMENTS

So many wonderful people provided technical information, editing, content ideas and access to people and resources. All of these efforts have contributed to the success of this book.

In an attempt to give credit to everyone who helped us complete the book, we would like to express our gratitude to:

Debbie Hourigan for reading and contributing to drafts in wee hours, serving us like royalty, and preparing days of sustenance lest we parish at the keyboard.

Our daughters, Jennifer Henderson and Caitlin Hourigan, who patiently edited multiple drafts.

Bob Bevard, Terry Vandewater, Rick Amme, Denise Sicking, Karen Quinn, Dr. Robert Giacalone, Jeff Lucas Nancy Lauterbach, Vonda Kurtz Ovaitt, Blake Lochrie, Charlotte Lee, MD., Laurie Calzada, and Carol Johnson for their candor, contributions and support.

Countless clients for their years of trusting collaboration and colleagues who have stretched and challenged us to continue raising the bar.

An abundance of friends and family who cheered us on.

Now we know how the people at the academy awards feel—if we forgot anyone, please let us know and we will make sure to include you in the next edition.

INTRODUCTION

When we began to write this book, we had no idea it would take on a life of its own. Originally, we intended to write a simple, enjoyable book with some realistic leadership advice on managing people and change.

As people began to read the book and provide feedback, we had no idea how many different observations and conclusions they would form about leadership. We would love to say this was all on purpose, but we know that during the writing process, we inadvertently added lessons learned from our years in the workforce, in roles from staff to executive, and from employee to external consultant. And, as is universally true, no matter what the story, people will interpret its meaning based on their own experiences.

Most readers told us they read the book twice and found new and different lessons on their second reading. And isn't that the way of life? We learn something new or gain a different perspective with each passing wave.

We were delighted to hear that people universally loved the character, Foot, and wished they had a mentor just like him. We were saddened to find how few said they ever had.

We hope you enjoy the book and look forward to any insights you would like to share.

So...Bon Voyage!
Enjoy your journey as you "Ride the Waves"!

Mike & Kathleen

Riding the Waves Without Getting Wet

Cruisin'

"A person has three choices in life. You can swim against the tide and get exhausted, or you can tread water and let the tide sweep you away, or you can swim with the tide, and let it take you where it wants you to go."

Diane Frolov & Andrew Schneider

Phillip Phelps was a man on the move. Only in his mid-thirties, he had already been a National Sales Manager, a VP of Operations and a VP of Sales and Marketing. No more

1

than one might expect from an Ivy League MBA, but the companies had been small. Now he stood at the apex of his career—on board the cruise ship *Southern Siren*, at a party in his honor. Phillip and his colleagues were celebrating his signing of the single biggest contract in the billion dollar company's history and, he was certain, his promotion to Senior Vice President.

So, for once, Phillip ignored the pulsing in his pocket and reached for a glass of champagne offered by a leather-skinned waiter with a graying beard and ponytail. *What a loser,* Phillip thought, *middle-aged and still working a teenager's job.* Then Phillip saw the diamond studs in the man's left ear. There were so many. He quickly counted them, *...and with seven ear studs and a ponytail, I can see why!* he thought. *A loser by design!*

Phillip looked out over the ballroom and was generally pleased by what he saw. The serving table was spread with sumptuous fare, including lobster and caviar, his favorites. At least *that* was first class, even if the ship itself had seen better days. He thought the ice sculpture of his new client's logo was a nice touch. The band was competent, although their uniforms were starting to fray around the cuffs. But he found the balloons and banners wholly inappropriate for such an important occasion.

Nonetheless, it was with a smile of self-satisfaction that Phillip straightened his tuxedo jacket and watched two of his direct reports take to the dance floor. The ballroom was filled with people who had worked on his project. But most of them really didn't deserve to be there, he thought, not when he had been forced to ride them as hard as he had to meet deadlines.

Now two of them were coming over to suck up. Phillip downed his flute of champagne to brace himself for the interaction. He had always been leery of becoming too social with his reports. He believed that it tended to erode their respect for his authority.

A balding man with a paunch and an almost-sincere smile stuck out a chunky hand. "Congratulations, Phillip," he said. "Rumor has it that the old man may be changing your name plate tonight."

"Your congratulations are a little premature, Frank, but thanks. I appreciate the thought," Phillip replied as he shook the man's hand.

"Me too," said the other report, sticking out his hand. "Congratulations."

"Thank you, Bob," Phillip replied mechanically.

"Listen, Phillip," said Frank, "now that we've landed this monster account, I was thinking that if we reorganized our service teams into ..."

Just then Phillip's pocket started vibrating again and he had to consciously keep his relief from becoming visible. Taking his cell phone out of his pocket brought the conversation to an immediate halt. "Excuse me, won't you..." said Phillip. And that was enough to send his reports scurrying. They knew how he was about his phone calls.

The display on his cell phone revealed that the call came from Arvin Cord, the company's plant manager, someone who definitely knew better than to call him here. "This better be important, Arvin," Phillip barked into the phone. "This is NOT a good time!"

"It is, Phillip," Arvin replied. "We just got those struts you subbed out and put 'em on the torsion tester."

"And?" Phillip snorted impatiently.

"And they're not up to specs!" Arvin reported anxiously. "They literally come apart under maximum load. We put some of the pieces under the microscope and they don't look right. I don't think there's any titanium in this alloy at all. We had to shut the line down."

Phillip lost it. "You WHAT!!?" he shouted.

Before Arvin could reply, Phillip was shocked back into control by the voice of his CEO behind him. "Problem, Phillip?" the CEO asked.

Phillip turned with a start, then mumbled a quiet, "I'll get back to you," into the phone and quickly put it in his pocket. "No, Roy, no problem," he said with his best aw-shucks grin. "Just a call from my broker—always calling with the latest hot tip."

After a hearty laugh, the CEO put his hand on Phillip's back and said, "Come with me, lad. I have something to say." Then he propelled Phillip toward a small stage set up at one end of the room. The CEO climbed up on stage and tapped his champagne flute with a spoon to get everyone's attention.

Once everyone had gathered around, he signaled toward the back of the room and waiters quickly made the rounds replenishing everyone's champagne. "Everyone raise your glass," he said, "because I want to propose a toast."

When all flutes were filled, the CEO raised his glass and said, "Ladies and gentlemen, we are here tonight to celebrate an accomplishment that will propel our company to a new threshold."

At this, everyone whistled, hooted and clinked their glasses with silverware until the CEO held up his hand to quiet them.

"And, everyone in this room tonight was an integral part of this accomplishment," he said with genuine sincerity. "So the first toast is to you! We couldn't have done it without you!"

The CEO drained his glass and held it out for the waiter to refill, and everyone else dutifully did the same, accompanied by more hoots and whistles, which Phillip found rather boorish.

"And now," the CEO continued, holding up his newly filled flute, "I want you to join me in toasting the man who put this landmark accomplishment together. Phillip, come on up here!"

There were only the sounds of some subdued glassware clinking and people snickering, subtly elbowing each other, as Phillip took the stage.

"While everybody gets a refill, let me tell you a little about this guy. When he first joined us, we expected great things from this hard-charging dynamo and, by golly, he's delivered. He's our top producer three-years running, one of the Springfield Chamber's Top Ten Young Executives, ProSell Magazine's Man of the Year, and now our new, all-time, sales record holder. To commemorate your achievements, Phillip, we'd like to present you with this solid gold, business card case..."

The CEO held up the case for all to see, then opened it so Phillip could peer inside.

"...filled with the business cards..." and then with fanfare, "...for our new Director of Business Development!"

Fighting back the expression of his shock and disappointment, the best Phillip could summon was a blank stare. Dead silence filled the room.

"*And,*" continued the CEO, taking an envelope from his inside jacket pocket, "it comes with a bonus check that I believe you'll find very pleasing."

He handed the check to Phillip. And as he did, Phillip's staff, rolling their eyes, exchanged quick glances. Still, there was silence—until the CEO pulled a whole stack of envelopes from his pocket and added, "In fact, I have bonus checks here for everybody in this room!"

Now the room erupted in hoots, whistles and the clinking together of fifty-seven flutes of champagne. Still a little dazed, Phillip held up his business card case and check like the applause was for him. He clinked flutes with the CEO, gulped down his champagne and left the stage to regain his composure and figure out what to do about this turn of events. What had gone wrong? Why hadn't they given him the position he deserved? Phillip knew he had to turn this around. He had to think—and answer the phone that had been vibrating in his pocket during the whole presentation.

"Hang on a second, Arvin," Phillip said into the phone. Then, using the phone for cover so that he could pass through the crowd, granting just the perfunctory smiles and nods, he made his way onto the ship's deck.

"Arvin, you've got to get that line back up and running *immediately*!" he shouted once out on deck. "No excuses! The contract has a bail-out clause if we don't deliver on time!"

"The struts are not up to specs, Phillip!" Arvin countered, "If we put them in they're going to fail! What does the contract say about *that*?!!"

Just then people started coming out onto the deck in twos and threes. In the still night air, Phillip could hear fragments of conversation from across the deck. "Yeah right, the Habitat house, he was there...actually swung a hammer." "Oh, come on," sarcastically, "you know he did that for show!" And a trace from another direction "...yeah, but I'd give it back for a transfer," followed by the sound of laughter, then a staccato, "sure he did...just long enough to figure out how to blame *you*!" So he moved farther away and lowered his voice.

"Look, Arvin, that tester puts a lot more load on those struts than they'll actually be under in normal use. They'll last for months, during which time we'll diligently have them retested. Then, if they really *aren't* the contracted alloy, we'll recall them before any harm is done, and the customer thanks us for our diligence and our ethics. We could be heroes, Arvin."

More conversation wafted over, somebody imitating someone in a deep self-important voice. "I don't care *what* your personal problems are! We have a *deadline* to meet!" More laughter followed.

At the same time, Arvin was saying, "Why don't we just tell the client what's happened, take our lumps, get some more time and do it right?"

Phillip replied, "Because that could jeopardize my..." but then snapped, "because it's easier to beg for forgiveness than it is to ask for permission, that's why!"

"I don't know, Phillip," Arvin worried, "people's lives could be in danger if these things fail."

Phillip caught another trace of conversation amplified by the champagne. "...*overboard*?!! Good riddance! That's what *I'd* say!" And again there was laughter.

"Trust me, Arvin," Phillip whispered. "I know what I'm doing. After this blows over, and I've been in my new position for awhile, I'm going to remember your loyalty. You know what I'm saying?"

"I hear what you're saying, Phillip," Arvin replied tentatively, "but—"

Phillip saw some people he thought were headed his way.

"I'll take full responsibility," Phillip said with authority. "Just get that line back up NOW! I've got to go." He snapped closed and pocketed the phone.

Phillip had to think this out. This situation could get way out of hand. His entire career could be at stake. Then there was the whole Senior VP thing. Somehow he had to convince the old man that he could be of greater value in a more senior position. But that would not matter if one of those struts failed prematurely. He had to think this out. Phillip slipped back into the ballroom for one last glass of champagne, and then headed for his state room.

His room was easy to spot. It was the one with the "Do Not Disturb" sign on the knob. He always left it on the door. He didn't like cleaning people in his room when he was gone. He wanted them there on *his* schedule. He had no sooner gained his retreat when his phone started vibrating again.

"NOW WHAT?!!!" he railed under his breath. "IS NOBODY IN THIS COMPANY COMPETENT BUT ME?" Incompetence sent Phillip's blood pressure soaring.

All of a sudden there was no air in the room. It was hot and he could feel the room closing in on him. Phillip was starting to sweat. He gulped the last of his champagne and headed for some fresh air.

By the time Phillip reached the deck, his head was spinning. He leaned against the railing to fish the phone out of his pocket. The night was cool, but he was sweating profusely. At the same time, he was both exasperated and shaken. His vision kept going in and out of focus. He could hear voices, but he couldn't tell how far away they were. Phillip closed his eyes and took a deep breath.

Then something happened.
He wasn't sure what, exactly, had happened,
but something definitely had happened.
Something bad.

All of a sudden he was falling in slow motion. *How odd,* he later remembered thinking while simultaneously feeling that he was actually still on deck. And he sort of *felt* himself thinking that if only he could open his eyes…then he hit the water.

In a panic, Phillip instinctively fought against his downward motion and, after what seemed an eternity, he arrested it and started fighting his way to the surface. When he finally emerged, Phillip was almost even with the ship's stern. "Help!" he shouted. "Someone help me!" But all Phillip heard in response was faint laughter and the roar of the ship's engines. Suddenly, he felt very cold and scared, but most of all, he felt alone. This time he had no one to act on his barked orders. He continued to shout, "Help! Someone help me!" The music swelled. He heard applause. The wind swallowed his words and an icy cavern of endless water swallowed him.

Back on board, the ponytailed waiter was on deck making his final rounds checking for abandoned champagne glasses when he heard a faint splash—and an even fainter call for help. Rushing to the port side railing, the waiter saw someone in the water. It looked like a man in a tuxedo. The waiter looked around for a life ring to throw but none were within reach. By now the man was astern and rapidly being left behind in the ship's wake. With no one close by to help, the waiter acted without thinking.

Instantly, he activated the self-launching mechanism on one of the lifeboats and jumped on as the boat was lowered over the side. Hanging on to the rigging that secured the boat's canvas cover, he fell with the boat and landed with a splash. He immediately started loosening the rigging and pulling back the canvas to get to the boat's controls. Once in, he uncovered the helm and pushed the ignition button for the motor—but all he got was a sickening click.

Phillip, meanwhile, had sobered up in a hurry. The sudden realization that he was alone in the middle of the South Pacific, watching his ship get smaller and smaller each time the chop allowed him to catch a glimpse of it, had canceled out the effects of the champagne in short order. Just as real panic was about to set in, he thought he saw something fall from the ship. "It had better be a life boat," he muttered angrily, and although he couldn't see anything over the waves, he thought, almost out loud, *it's about time! Now get your butt over here and rescue me!*

Phillip started thinking about how he would spin this to his advantage. He figured that almost losing him would make his

CEO appreciate him even more and he didn't want to dilute that. But, he thought, milking it might create a backlash on him. So he decided he would play it with macho bravado, as just a funny thing that happened on the way to Tahiti, something to laugh about when he and the CEO were taking a steam down at the club. Phillip could almost hear the water-cooler conversation about how brave and self-effacing he was to react like that. He definitely could spin this to his advantage—only where was that stupid lifeboat?

The stupid lifeboat was dead in the water, but the waiter viewed the situation philosophically. After all, what can you expect from a battery that's not used for months on end? The boat was equipped with oars, but there was no way he could both row and keep a lookout for someone in the water. So the waiter did the next best thing—he started yelling.

With the sound of the ship's engines now just a distant hum, Phillip had no trouble hearing the waiter's call. "Ahoy! Ahoy! Over here! Follow the sound of my voice! Ahoy!" He just had trouble understanding. Figuring that only crew members would know how to launch a lifeboat, after all, did they really expect *him* to come to *them*? After all, *they* had the boat, not him. *They* were the ones paid to do this, not him. That kind of service would earn *somebody* a very nasty phone call to the head of the cruise line. That was for sure! But, as he was already growing weary from fighting the waves, he started swimming toward the sound.

After five minutes that seemed like fifty, Phillip reached the boat. The waiter pulled him aboard, saying with a genuine sense of relief, "Whoa, Dude! Am I glad to see you! I thought you were a goner! "

"Well I would have been if I hadn't known how to swim, now wouldn't I?" Phillip replied with irritation. "Don't you know how to operate this boat?"

"Battery's dead, man," said the waiter matter-of-factly. "Manual start doesn't work either. Must'a been awhile since this baby was maintenanced. There was nothing I could do but hope you could hear me—and I'm sure glad you did!"

"I'll bet you are! It saved you from a BIG lawsuit. Now get the ship on the radio so we can get out of here!"

"No radio, man. Not even a flare gun. I checked."

Phillip was stunned. He simply could not believe this was happening. This sort of thing did *not* happen to *him*. He did *not* permit it. So watching the lights of the ship disappear over the horizon infuriated him—and he found himself yelling. "Are you trying to tell me that we're adrift, in the middle of the ocean, with *no motor* and *no radio*? What kind of incompetent fool are you?!!"

"The kind it took to rescue *you*, pal. I work as a waiter. I don't maintain the lifeboats. And I was the only one who saw you go over. If I hadn't launched when I did, you'd be shark bait now."

That gave Phillip pause. He grudgingly admitted—to himself—that he *was* glad to be in a boat instead of in the water. The perplexed look on Phillip's face put a huge grin on the waiter's.

"But, hey, man, we do have a beautiful night for it! I never get tired of looking at the stars out here."

Phillip stared back in disbelief. Here they were, in a life-threatening situation and this aging hippie was acting like he was on vacation. *I'm not only adrift,* he thought, *I'm adrift with an idiot!*

Then the idiot looked Phillip in the eye and shook his hand. For a moment a surprised Phillip sensed a cool professionalism but quickly dismissed it.

"I'm Foot."

The First Wave

"Circumstances do not make the man,
they reveal him."

James Allen

He could barely see him in the light of the half-moon. Phillip shook Foot's hand halfheartedly. "Is that your first name or your last name?" Phillip asked disdainfully.

"It's what people call me," Foot replied. "And you?"

"Phelps. Phillip Phelps," he replied, then sarcastically adding, "Director of *Stinking* Business *Stinking* Development for—"

"Why do you say it that way?" Foot interrupted.

"Because it's *not* the position I deserve after *all I've done*, that's why!" Phillip said bitterly. Then he pulled the solid gold, business card case out of his pocket and held it so the moonlight glinted off its surface. "I just landed them the single biggest contract in their stinking history and all I got was a mediocre party on board a discount cruise line, a meaningless new title and this...trinket!" And with that Phillip drew his arm back to heave the case into the sea—but suddenly Foot was on top of him pinning his arm to his chest.

"Whoa, man! What are you doing?!!" Foot shouted.

Even in the dim light, Foot could make out a look of total incomprehension on Phillip's face. "We don't know how long we're going to be out here," Foot explained patiently, "or what we're going to have to do to survive—and we can't afford to waste any resources we have. Like the man said, "'You don't miss your water 'til the well runs dry.'[1]"

"All right! All right!" Phillip protested. "Get off me and I'll *give* it to you."

"Sorry, man," said Foot climbing off Phillip. "Just a gut reaction, you know."

"Here," said Phillip, handing Foot the meaningless case.

Foot took the case and put it in his pocket. "I'll take good care of it. You might feel differently about it later." Then he quickly added, "Hey, you need to get out of those wet clothes!" Foot started rummaging around underneath the canvas that still covered the bow of the boat and emerged with a blanket. "I thought I felt a blanket under here!"

Foot handed the blanket to Phillip who took it gratefully and began to disrobe. "You didn't feel a flashlight in there, did you?" Phillip asked.

"As a matter of fact, I did!" Foot responded cheerfully.

"Then how about a little light here?"

"Dead batteries."

"You get what you pay for."

While Phillip took off his clothes, Foot groped around in the stern of the boat until he found the sea anchor and threw it into the ocean. The splash alarmed Phillip. "What was that?!"

"Sea anchor," Foot responded. "It'll keep us turned into the waves in case the wind comes up tonight."

"We're not going to be here that long," Phillip arrogantly assured him.

"What makes you think so?" Foot asked.

"Because someone will see the missing life boat or realize one of us is gone, and they'll come back and pick us up," he said, with his customary iron-willed self-confidence returning.

"Well…" Foot said thoughtfully, "Maybe. But, unfortunately, these particular self-launching life boats have been known to short out and launch themselves. They lost one about six months ago that way. And as for being missed, tomorrow's my day off, and I usually spend that reading. They won't miss me for 24 hours. How about you?"

Then Phillip remembered the sign hanging on his stateroom door. "Oh, no," he realized, "There's a 'Do Not Disturb' sign on my door. They won't miss me either."

"Well, then," Foot said quietly, "I suggest we get as comfortable as we can—because we're going to need all the rest we can get." Then he looked up at the sky and added, "But don't we have a great night for it!?"

They floated in silence for awhile, each lost in his own thoughts, Foot thinking about what lay ahead, Phillip worrying about what lay behind—and how to get out of being blamed for the struts situation. He had to stay out in front of this thing with the struts. He had to be the one to discover the flaw and subsequently initiate the recall. He knew he could baffle the client into believing it was just an inconvenience. He needed to make sure Arvin didn't lose his nerve, but his cell phone was at the bottom of the ocean. So he *had* to get back quickly. Surely, *somebody* would...

"Why did you fall overboard?" Foot asked out of nowhere.

Defensively, Phillip snapped, not quite certain how he fell overboard, "*Why*? What do you mean *why*? It was an accident. *Obviously*. What else could it have been?!"

Foot issued a skeptical, "Hmmmmm."

"What is *that* supposed to mean?" Phillip asked impatiently.

"I just don't believe in accidents. That's all."

"What do you mean you don't *believe* in accidents? What's not to believe in? You step on a banana peel, you go down. Cause and effect. It's simple," responded Phillip indignantly.

"Look out there on the water," Foot said quietly.

"What?"

"Look out there on the water."

Phillip looked out over the quietly rolling sea.

"OK, I'm looking. What am I looking at?"

"See the reflection of the moon on the water?"

"Yeah. So?"

"Is it caused by the moon or by the water?"

That gave Phillip a pause, but not a long one. "It's *caused* by the light from the moon bouncing off the water and into your eye. And you can dissect that any way you like."

"Isn't it also caused by the light-sensitive cells on your retina?" queried Foot adding, "and the gravity of the earth that keeps the moon in orbit—and the nuclear fusion on the sun that provides the light—and the rotation of the earth that creates the night—and…"

Now Phillip became really irritated. "So what? What's your

point? How can you not understand what an accident is? You think I jumped over? Is that what you think? You think I did it on purpose? Just out for a midnight swim? Is that it? Or maybe you think—" and there Phillip stopped abruptly, suddenly as pale as the moonlight. "Oh my God!" he whispered as he remembered the bits and pieces of conversation he'd overheard on board the ship. "Is *that* what you really think? You think somebody *pushed* me overboard?"

Foot paused a second, then answered very clearly, "No, I didn't think that at all. But *you did*. What made *you* think of that?"

Phillip was at a loss. "I... don't know." He wasn't about to tell this idiot that his people hated him. Besides, the whole idea was preposterous. "But now that I think about it, that *couldn't* have happened," Phillip said incredulously.

"Why not?"

"It just couldn't, that's all."

"So how *did* it happen?"

"I'm...not sure. I don't really remember. Probably a post-traumatic stress reaction."

"Hmmm..." Foot replied skeptically. "What *do* you remember?"

"I was out on deck, alone, so that I could have a private and very urgent telephone conversation. I remember leaning against the railing to get out my phone…and I remember taking a deep breath to clear my head and…then I thought I heard voices…and then…all of a sudden I was falling in slow motion. I must have gotten dizzy or lost my footing or my balance or…" now Phillip's face lit up. "Or *probably* the railing on that rotting tub of a cruise ship broke!" Phillip was elated to have found a plausible explanation. "*That's* probably the *real* cause! An *accident*, just like I said, probably the result of criminal negligence. We'll let the lawyers sort that one out," he said with self-satisfaction.

"Why didn't you make the call from your cabin?"

"It was stuffy in there. I couldn't catch my breath it was so stifling. That's *more* grounds for a charge of negligence."

"Why not make the call from the ballroom where the light's better? Everybody was cleared out by then."

"I told you, the call was *private*."

"You also said 'urgent.' What was so urgent about it?"

"You wouldn't understand. It has to do with the operation of a manufacturing plant that covers the better part of a square mile."

"Try me. You might be surprised."

"Well, if you must know, my plant manager had shut down our production line due to a minor problem and his actions threatened to jeopardize a huge contract—*my* contract. And I couldn't let that happen."

"What was the minor problem?"

"A subcontractor supplied some parts that the plant manager thought weren't up to specs. It happens all the time."

"Who contracted the subcontractor?"

"I did."

"Why did you choose *that* supplier?"

Now Phillip was becoming irritated again. "Lots of reasons," he snapped.

"Like what?" Foot persisted.

"Cost, quality, delivery time—lots of reasons."

"Everybody says they provide those things. Why did you give *this* supplier the contract?"

Now Phillip became defensive—and angry. "Hey! I don't have to answer to you. This is none of your business. I had incentives to go with the company I chose (one of Foot's eyebrows went up at that) and it was *my* decision to make and that's all there is to it. Understand?"

"Whoa!" Foot said soothingly. "I didn't mean to get you all agitated. I was just curious about why you fell overboard because *your* going overboard caused *me* to go overboard. And now, as the saying goes, we're both in the same boat, you know?"

"Well I hope you got your answer," Phillip snorted.

"I think I did."

"Good," Phillip said with finality. But then curiosity got the better of him and he added, "What might that be?"

"Well, correct me if I'm wrong...you were out on deck, all alone, because you needed to make a call that you couldn't afford to have anyone else to hear, and you couldn't make the call from your room because you felt unwell. You felt *so unwell* that you needed to lean against the railing to steady yourself, a condition that might be explained by the champagne you drank or extreme fatigue or, just possibly, from the enormous stress that comes from having taken a kickback from a supplier who also was unscrupulous enough to double-cross you and supply substandard parts. And..."

"YOU'RE AN IDIOT!" Phillip shouted.

"And," Foot persisted, "the thought that you might have been pushed seems plausible because you probably stepped all over the people who work for you in the process. But..."

"YOU'RE A JACKASS!" Phillip screamed. "If you ever repeat one word of that ridiculous accusation to any living soul on this planet, I will sue you for everything you ever thought about having! You understand me?"

"But," Foot went on with complete equanimity, "I think—"

"I DON"T CARE WHAT YOU THINK! DIDN'T I MAKE MYSELF CLEAR?"

Foot sighed contentedly as he settled back into a fold of

canvas.

"I think you threw yourself overboard."

The Second Wave

"We cannot live only for ourselves. A thousand fibers connect us with our fellow-men; and along those fibers, as sympathetic threads, our actions run as causes, and they come back to us as effects."

Herman Melville

The next day took Phillip by surprise. He was certain he had not slept at all. His mind had been much too busy trying to crisis manage all the potentially damaging situations he suddenly had to confront. Yet the sunlight on his face woke him abruptly.

Foot met Phillip's awakening with an open grin that held no memory of the rancor Phillip had expressed the night before. "Good morning, sir!" he said playfully. "How about some eggs and hotcakes, with a side of bacon and a cup of steaming hot coffee?"

Phillip was not amused. "Are my clothes dry?" he muttered, as he searched for his trousers.

"Yes, sir!" Foot responded. "All laid out for you just where you left them!"

Phillip found his pants and shirt just dry enough to put on and did so. Foot was dressed only in a pair of cheesy boxer shorts printed with surfers and palm trees. He was sitting in the bow of the boat, fiddling with something in a small plastic box. "Is there *anything* to eat?" Phillip inquired.

"Well, we have good news and bad news in that department," Foot said calmly. "The good news is that this boat came equipped with stores to last ten people for a month. The bad news is that rats ate most of it—and I suspect that the crew has been helping themselves to it for awhile as well. All that's left is four cans of peaches, a swollen can of Spam two years out of date and two liters of bottled water."

"That's all!??" Phillip complained. "What kind of a—" Phillip started to launch a tirade, but stopped himself when he remembered that he had decided the night before to try to schmooze Foot to keep him from spouting wild theories about kickbacks when they were rescued. So he abruptly changed the subject. "Why do people call you Foot?" he said, in his best simulation of sincerity.

"Because I'm a goofy-foot," Foot responded.

Phillip looked at Foot's feet but saw nothing out of the ordinary. "Your feet look perfectly normal to me," he said.

"I'm a surfer," Foot replied. "That means I surf with my right foot forward instead of my left. Surfers call that a 'goofy foot'."

"Oh, I see," Phillip said, spotting an opportunity to advance the schmooze, "They're '*goofing*' on you, is that it?"

Foot raised an eyebrow and smiled slightly, a good sign.

"Maybe," he said, "but I don't mind. Being a goofy foot gives me a different look at the beach than most surfers get, a little different perspective, you know?"

"How long have you been a waiter?" Phillip continued, sensing that Foot was going for it.

"I'm *not* a waiter," Foot said patiently. "I'm a surfer. Waiting tables is what I *do*, not what I *am*." Then Foot held up what he had been fiddling with, a length of fishing line with a hook and small weight attached. "Are you a fisherman?" he asked.

"Where'd you get that?" Phillip asked.

"Ship's stores. We've got line, hooks, weights, even a Swiss Army knife, everything we need to catch our breakfast except bait. But I think a bit of rancid Spam might just do the trick."

And with that Foot tore the top off the can of Spam and, holding his breath, slipped a hunk of it onto the hook, keeping the spoiled meat as far away as possible.

Once the hook was baited, Foot threw it overboard and payed out the line until he felt it was enough, and then handed it to Phillip.

"Oh, no, I couldn't," Phillip said, "I've never…" But Foot left the line in his hands.

"Give a man a fish and you feed him for a day, teach a man to fish—"[2] Foot quoted.

"No, you don't understand," Phillip protested, "I don't, ah…" This was not going well. They were getting too far afield and Phillip didn't want to be distracted. "I mean, isn't this more your area of responsibility?" he said as diplomatically as he could.

"Why? Because I work as a waiter?" Foot said. Amused by this line of reasoning, he continued, "Since I serve fish it should be my responsibility to catch them? Is that it? I've got news for you, shipmate. According to maritime law, as a ship's employee and a card-carrying member of the seafarers union, I am now *Captain* of this vessel and *you* are the crew! I can make you walk the plank if you don't help out."

Phillip stared at Foot blankly as he weighed his options. He decided this was not the battle to fight. Recalling his earlier impression of this guy with the seven earrings, he thought Foot might be a worthy adversary. There still the kickback accusation to take care of, so he said, "Ok, what do

I do?"

"Just wrap the line around something to make a handle and hang on to it. When you feel something tug, tug back hard and then pull it in. I'll cut you a couple of pieces of canvas to use as gloves."

Not finding anything else at hand, Phillip tied the line around one of his $460 black Gucci loafers, counting on his sacrifice for the cause to not go unnoticed.

But Foot just busied himself with the boat's canvas cover, first cutting Phillip's 'gloves' and then cutting a much bigger piece. Phillip felt the gentle pull of the waves on the line as the bait was washed astern of the boat. He watched the sunlight play on the water as the line payed out and for a brief moment allowed himself to be mesmerized by the gentle roll of the boat, the soft breeze and the water washing over the line. His mind relaxed...,but he roughly yanked himself out of it and got back to business.

"Listen," Phillip said contritely, "about last night... I hope you didn't take what I was saying personally, because I was really stressed out and may have said some things that—"

"You mean about my being an idiot and your plans to sue me? Why should I take that personally?" Foot teased.

"Yeah, well, like I said, I was... not myself last night. And, by the way, just for the record, I *did not* take a kickback."

"Then what was the 'incentive' you mentioned?" Foot asked with a twinkle in his eye.

For reasons he could not have explained, Phillip found himself telling at least part of the truth. "It was just the use of a condo on Oahu and a hunting lodge at Jackson Hole, that's all," Phillip confessed, "no big deal, really, just normal business perks."

"But enough to tempt you into making a bad decision, huh?"

"Look, you just don't understand how business is…"

"You take a little advantage, he takes a little advantage and the cost has to be made up *somewhere*. Isn't that about it? You're like the surfer who thinks he can ride the waves without getting wet."

"Hey! I still don't know *for sure* that those struts are a bad alloy and, besides, I had *no way of knowing* that he might—" stopping himself, as he sensed that Foot wasn't buying this.

"No way of knowing? Are you sure? Sounds to me like you could use a dose of 'eddy thinking'."

"Who's Eddie?" Phillip asked, with growing annoyance.

"Not who, but what," Foot responded evenly. "When you throw a stone into a pond what happens? The stone makes ripples in the water that will spread out until they wash over your feet if you just stand there. You know that when you throw it in. And when you decide to accept a little personal 'perk,' you throw a stone into a pond. So you shouldn't be surprised when the ripples come back and soak your Gucci's. What goes around comes around, you know?"

All Phillip could say in response was to weakly repeat, "I didn't take a kickback." Then they lapsed into silence, Foot absorbed with his canvas and Phillip wondering how this itinerate waiter kept getting the better of him, and trying not to think about the growling in his stomach.

At high noon, Foot put down his canvas, took a sextant out of a storage compartment and started taking a sighting.

"What, exactly, are you doing?" Phillip asked.

"Calculating our latitude," Foot responded.

"Why?"

"Because no matter where you want to go, you've got to start from where you are."

"Go? What do you mean 'go?' Shouldn't we stay put so they can find us?"

"By the time they discover we're gone, the ship will be more than a hundred miles away. Factoring in wind and currents," he mentally calculated, "they'll have more than a thousand square miles to search. Pago Pago is the nearest port with a rescue plane. They'll use most of their fuel coming and going from the search area. With our limited stores, we're not going to last nearly as long as it might take them to find us."

"So just where do you propose we 'go'?"

"South."

"Why south?"

Phillip began to challenge Foot's authority. He was uncomfortable because he hadn't been able to size him up in his usual fashion. Accustomed to being able to quickly sum up his opponents, Foot didn't easily fit into one of Phillip's predefined categories.

"Two reasons. One, according to the reading I just made, we're north of the commercial shipping lanes. That's where we just might get spotted by a passing freighter. And two, look out over the water and tell me what you see."

"I see water, endless water. What am I supposed to see?"

"Well, first, you might see the direction of the chop. That's caused by the wind. But then, if you look at the sea as a whole and kind of watch it for awhile, you can see that there are big swells moving under the chop from west to east. They're caused by the spinning of the earth. See them?"

Phillip looked and sure enough, after awhile he saw them. "Yes! I see them! But, so what?"

"Well, if you look very carefully, you can also see a set of smaller swells, running at an angle to the big ones. Do you see them?"

Phillip looked as hard as he could, but still could not see the smaller swells. "No," he said. "I don't."

"Well, it takes some practice. But, what those swells are telling us is that there's an island somewhere to the south. The smaller swells are ripples made by the big swells bouncing off the island."

Phillip looked again, skeptical that Foot was able to see an island somewhere over the horizon. "I still can't see what you're talking about," he complained.

"Like I said, it takes practice," said Foot, "but I recommend that you keep trying, because sometimes the most important ripples are the ones that are hardest to see."

Phillip was impressed, but unconvinced. "Ok, let's suppose there *is* an island somewhere 'over the rainbow' to the south of us," he said cynically. "How do you propose we get there—by rowing? How long do you think we could keep that up? Probably just long enough to get out of the search area! No. I say we stay where we are and wait to be rescued."

"No good," said Foot with finality. "As Mr. Dylan once said, 'He not busy being born is busy dying.'[3] If we stay, we die. If we go, we at least stand a chance."

Phillip considered this, but it still seemed nonsensical. "No," he said with equal finality. "You may consider yourself the 'captain' and all, but don't forget, I'm *the customer!* And I say we stay!"

"You don't adapt to change very well, do you?" Foot chided. "So let me put it this way, Matie," he said, dropping into an impersonation of Long John Silver. "Any member o' me crew who don't do what his kindly, old Cap'n asks don't get no rations t'night! And don't be forgettin'... *I've* got the knife!" Then he whipped out the Swiss Army knife with the can opener extended and waved it about menacingly while laughing and doing his best impression of a mad man.

Phillip decided this *was* the battle to fight. "Well *I'm* not rowing anywhere," he declared defiantly.

"Well, fortunate for you," Long John Foot replied, "I ain't asked you to, has I, Matey?"

So what was all that about? wondered Phillip, since the end result was staying put just as he had insisted. Foot quickly had gone back to working with the canvas, so Phillip decided to be a gracious winner and let it lie.

They drifted along in silence until sometime in the late afternoon, when the breeze died, and the sun beat down unmercifully. Phillip was determined to hold out as long as Foot, but this was too much. "How about a drink?" he said, finally.

"Not 'til tonight," Foot replied. "We'll retain more of it then."

Becalmed and parched, time seemed to stand still. Phillip decided some idle conversation would help pass the time, so he asked the question he had been dying to ask.

"Mind if I ask you a personal question?" Phillip inquired.

"Go for it," Foot replied amiably.

"What's with those seven earrings you wear? Doesn't that sort of...limit your possibilities?"

"As a surfer? No way, man. I wear seven earrings as a reminder of lessons learned. You see, in surfing lore, waves come in sets of seven as the swells I showed you reach the shore. These earrings identify me as a serious surfer, a life-surfer, you know? They've gotten me free drinks, invaluable experiences and places to stay all over the world."

"I always thought of surfing as a young man's game. How long do you think you'll be able to be a surfer?"

"Hey, man, you can be a surfer from shore. It's more in the head than in the water."

That caught Phillip by surprise. In fact, he had to admit, this guy was *full* of surprises. "Oh, yeah? How's that?"

Now, for the first time all day, except for when he was using the sextant, Foot put down his canvas.

"I'm from Joplin, Missouri," Foot said, "so I didn't start surfing 'til I was 22. I was a graduate student at Stanford, in the MBA program, no less, when a friend talked me into trying it. I didn't get up for more than a few seconds at a time that first day, but there was something about it, something more than just the rush, that made me want to do it again. So I kept at it and, a couple of weeks later, I rode my first wave all the way to shore—and when I did..." now Foot got a faraway look in his eyes and seemed to be talking more to the ocean than to Phillip, "...the feeling I got was like nothing else I had ever felt. If religion is the way we relate ourselves to the rest of the universe, then it was a sure-enough religious experience—because I never felt more alive, more in tune with the world around me or more deeply and profoundly connected to the whole miraculous universe than I did out there on that wave."

Now Foot's voice took on a soft, reverent quality, like someone speaking in church. "See, you can't surf and think at the same time. If you do, you'll wipe out. The wave has the power of a freight train and it's constantly changing. To keep your balance, you have to change with it, making so many tiny adjustments to your balance and position so fast that you can't possibly do it consciously. You have to become one with that wave, feeling it, sensing it on a deeper level than your conscious mind can go. You have to react spontaneously, maintaining perfect balance at every instant, faster than you can think. And when you do, the most incredible thing happens. The barrier between you and the rest of the universe dissolves and you experience life directly, without the constant stream of internal dialogue, thoughts, fears, and expectations that are always there, in between us and life, coloring our sensations and altering our perceptions until we only experience life 'through a glass, darkly.'[4]"

"And I've found it to be true not only for waves of water but for waves of other kinds, too," he continued, "like the waves of success and failure, love and hate, ignorance and knowledge that have the power to wipe us out at any minute. It's all about keeping your balance, you know? So I'll be a surfer as long as I live. It's the way I relate."

Then Foot looked over at Phillip and asked, "How about you? How do you relate?" And Phillip found himself in the unfamiliar and uncomfortable position of not knowing what to say, so he dodged the question by being droll.

"Me?" he said, "I'm a fisherman."

At that, Foot smiled a huge smile and said, "That's the spirit! There may be hope for you yet!" Then he went back to his canvas.

That evening they shared six peach slices and had a small cup of water each. Foot said, "At this rate we have three more days of rations." Then, he added," We will have to start drinking our own urine." When Phillip heard that, he fully realized, for the first time, the reality of their situation. Phillip also experienced, for the first time in his life, what a panic attack felt like.

A band of fear cinched his chest, wringing the air from his lungs, and his pounding heart lunged to the base of his throat, all but choking off his last gasp of air. Phillip's mind, like a live electrical wire downed in a storm, danced white hot from scene to scene, demanding an answer as to how the devil he wound up here.

He had dutifully followed the plan, swallowed his "foolish pipe dreams" to become his father's "success." He could hear his dad now... "You even screwed up your own promotion!" Phillip could even see the look of disdain on his father's face.

Donald Phelps was a force that no one dared challenge. He had scratched his way to the top and he was determined that any kid of his would start there. He had demanded Phillip attend the best prep schools, compete with the elite, and live up to stratospheric expectations, when, no matter what he accomplished, Phillip never quite did enough. "No excuses; failure is not an option!" Often this was the sum total of communication from his father.

Power was purpose in Donald's world. His political aspirations meant family life in a privileged fishbowl. Phillip was forced to attend fundraisers and appearances, serving his role in the family portrait to manufacture the image that fed the public relations machine. As long as he could remember, Phillip had been a puppet to amuse the cronies on his father's stage.

Phillip had been a happy kid. He loved reading, music and gathering friends to act out shows in the backyard, complete with a blanket thrown over the swing set to create curtains. He had a cheap guitar and the Casio keyboard his grandmother had given him on his sixth birthday. He had been something of a musical prodigy. There wasn't anything Phillip heard—classical, jazz or rock—that he couldn't play by ear. It occurred to him, now, that he couldn't recall a happier time in his life.

As a teenager, Phillip's greatest passion was to pursue his role as a gifted singer, songwriter, and lead guitarist for a small, yet successful rock band, which was in the eyes of his parents a totally unworthy occupation. For this, he had experienced the pain of retribution for bucking the system. When he wanted to pursue music in college, his father had delivered a crushing ultimatum. And now, Phillip's mind was thrust back to that moment.

"You want to be some doped up guitar jockey? Fine. You're on your own. Don't expect an ounce of support from me! I didn't bust my hump to let you be some glorified music junkie." Phillip's stomach churned as he recalled how this had digressed into an inventory of all the suffering Donald had gone through, supposedly for his benefit.

"Get over it and get the business degree. You don't think I'm turning over the reigns of the company to some deluded dream chaser, do you?" Donald continued to berate his son, not looking for an answer. Most of their conversations had been one-sided and most of the questions had been rhetorical. Donald always had the answers. All of them.

Phillip had complied. This was what people did for Donald. They complied or they left. Phillip wasn't a fighter, nor was he willing to leave his well-feathered nest. It was a foregone conclusion that Phillip would attend Donald's alma mater and join his fraternity. He would follow the course of studies his father dictated. He attended the best prep schools and, with a sharp mind and quick wit, had just coasted by in his coursework. He paid his dues, checked off the boxes on the mandatory list, partied with his frat brothers and did the gig. While living a life of privilege and entitlement, Phillip's engagement with his own interests soon diminished.

In short, Phillip Phelps had become a product of what money can sometimes produce—an elitist snob—entitled, not by what he earned but by what was bought for him.

"I'm not sure you belong here," said a distant Donald Phelps to his newly minted MBA son. Those words still sent a wrenching blade of pain through Phillip's gut. Phillip had been leveled once again after jumping through his father's ever higher hoops. Donald denied Phillip his promised position in the company and told him to go prove himself elsewhere, coldly dismissing his son from his office.

It was the same old trick, the carrot and the stick, a desperate-to-please Phillip had fallen for all his life. His father seemed to delight in jerking the carrot out of his grasp at the eleventh hour.

Still battling for air and fearing the reality of what Foot had said, Phillip railed at the predicament he was in. It had taken him years to prove his dad wrong. He had finally scratched and crawled his way to some recognition and he wasn't about to lose it now.

Phillip's mind continued to throb with one painful memory after another until somewhere in the midst of this excruciating review he mercifully passed out.

The Third Wave

"Justice is always violent to the party offending, for every man is innocent in his own eyes."

Daniel Defoe

Phillip woke up in a fetal position hugging his fishing shoe. Foot was already awake, working with his canvas and looking at Phillip with a cocked head. Phillip didn't remember falling asleep, only of lying there with waves of panic crashing over him. Now that he was awake, the panic was gone but its shadow still lingered. He surveyed his surroundings and thought things looked different somehow.

There was a clarity and a brightness that made everything more vivid. Phillip thought it must have something to do with the quality of the morning light.

"Rough night?" Foot asked.

"No. Why?" Phillip responded.

"Because of all the shouting you were doing. You seemed tormented. But maybe it was just the peaches on an empty stomach," Foot offered.

"Yeah, maybe so," Phillip said dismissively, once again lost in the memories that were still so fresh, so agonizingly real. He had given up his own goals, done what he was supposed to do, and had not felt one shred of passion or fulfillment in anything he had done to get here.

He thought about the people back on the boat. They were there because it was their choice, he thought. What options had he been given? He was envious of their choices and angered by his own.

Trying to shake it off, a visibly depleted Phillip asked, "What's for breakfast?"

"Whatever's on the end of your fishing line," Foot said with a laugh.

Phillip pulled in the line and found a bare hook. "Guess I'm not much of a fisherman," Phillip said. "Too far outside my area of expertise, I suppose. Why don't you take a shot at it?" But Foot just passed Phillip the Spam.

"A real fisherman never wastes time regretting a bare hook. Bait up, dude," Foot said reassuringly.

Phillip took the can, reluctantly snagged a hunk of rancid meat on the hook and threw it back in the water, then tried to hand the line to Foot. "Really, Foot, you are probably much better at this than I am," he whined.

"Sorry, Matey, your Cap'n has other duties," Long John Foot said as he went back to his canvas.

Phillip was about to protest when his shoe tried to leap from his hand. At first, he was so astonished that it was all he could do to hang on. Then, instinctively, he began pulling back against the surprisingly strong tug at the other end of the line.

Foot shouted with glee, "Thar' she blows! Grab your gloves and haul 'er in, man!"

Phillip made a grab for the scraps of canvas with one hand while hanging on to his Gucci fishing pole with the other and soon managed to wrap one bare hand with the canvas. Hand over hand, he began to bring the fish closer, feeling its every twist and tug with exquisite acuity. He noticed the way the sunlight sparkled on the water, the freshness of the morning air, the way the boat seemed to dance on the choppy water, the energy surging through his body, all together, all at once—and Phillip felt more alive than he could ever remember feeling.

When he got the fish close to the boat, Foot was already in position, leaning over the side with the Swiss Army knife under the water. Then, almost as soon as Phillip saw the fish, shining with incredible iridescence just under the surface, Foot made one sure upward thrust and impaled the fish on his knife, just under its lower jaw.

It was a beautiful, two-pound mahi-mahi. Before Phillip could even catch his breath, Foot had it gutted and filleted and was handing Phillip a big piece of fish. Phillip was starving but somehow this slab of raw meat just didn't ring his dinner bell. Foot saw him hesitate and said, "Wait." Then he took the fillet from Phillip and with the skill of a fine sushi chef, cut it into small strips and rolled them up. "There you are, sir," Foot said with a flourish. Phillip found this to be the most hilarious thing he had ever experienced.

Phillip laughed so hard that he fell down. He laughed convulsively and with total abandon. Even though the joke was on him, he laughed with a joy he didn't know he possessed. When he finally regained his composure, he took the makeshift sushi from Foot and said, "Do you have any wasabi to go with that?" And for the first time, they shared a long, hearty belly laugh together.

After devouring his sushi, Phillip felt much better and finally took an interest in what Foot was doing. "What's that you've been working on?" he asked, as he threw his rebaited hook overboard.

"It's a surprise," Foot said. "It'll be finished in a couple more hours. I'll show it to you then."

Phillip figured it was some sort of awning to shade them from the sun and make them more comfortable as they waited for rescue, but he didn't spoil the surprise. Instead, he asked, "So did you ever finish your MBA?"

"Nope," Foot responded without looking up. "Once I experienced surfing, I knew what I wanted to do with my life, and that's what I've done. I've been all over the world, working my way from one surfing beach to another. I've surfed them all, Big Sur, Oahu, the Gold Coast, even Jeffrey's Bay on the coast of South Africa where the waves are so long and perfect you can ride for hours. It's been a great life, too. What about you? Where are you coming from?"

Asking Phillip about himself was like asking Richard Simmons about exercise. "Well, after I got my MBA," he began, "I accepted a market research position with a machine tool manufacturer, doubled revenues in only two years and was promoted to National Sales Manager."

"Why did you leave?"

"Unenlightened management. They didn't understand pricing, kept telling me I wasn't building enough margin into my sales. My job was to make sales. Their job was to make a profit from those sales—and they just didn't know how to do it. The concept of cost control was beyond them. So I left."

"Where'd you go next?"

"Straight to the headhunter, who got me a position as VP of Operations for an air-conditioning manufacturer. In three years, I virtually doubled productivity."

"Why'd you leave there?"

"Their Human Resources department kept working against me, kept sending me people who just weren't up to the challenge."

"Um, hmm, where to then?"

"From there, I accepted a position as VP of Sales and Marketing for an Auto Parts retail chain with sagging sales. I reorganized that company from top to bottom, chopped out the deadwood, financed the opening of fifty new stores, and increased market share by five percent."

"What happened to that?"

"Lack of vision. A company in expansion mode has to expect a temporary drain on capital resources. Sometimes unscheduled financing has to be secured to complete an expansion plan. But it's worth it because first you capture market share, then you capture profits. The board of that company just didn't have the guts for an aggressive growth plan. But I had a nice parachute clause with those guys. I came out all right."

"Then where?"

"From there to my present position as…" Phillip's voice took on a hard edge, "…Director of Business *Stinking* Development."

"And now your biggest account is in jeopardy because your supplier let you down and your plant manager has no nerve and your people are whiners and your boss is holding you back. Right?"

"Something like that."

"So what position would you rather have, not now, but say when you're my age. What do you want to be when you're fifty?"

Phillip didn't hesitate. "By the time I'm fifty," he said confidently, "I intend to have a condo in Aspen, a house on Lake Tahoe, a penthouse wherever my company is headquartered, a Ferrari, and a ten-million dollar portfolio."

"Yeah, but I asked you what you wanted to *be*, not what you wanted to *have*."

"Ok, I want to *be* the CEO of a major corporation."

"A leader?"

"No, *the* leader."

"Well, then, you better turn the ambition boat around, buddy, 'cause you're headed in the wrong direction," Foot proclaimed.

"What does that mean?" Phillip asked defensively.

"I mean you're a walking Peter Principle!" Foot said with a grin.

"I beg your pardon?" Phillip snapped back indignantly.

"Let me see if I have this right. At your first rodeo, you tried to sell below cost and make it up in volume and when it didn't work you blamed your operations guy. But with the right spin and a good headhunter you moved up from there to a company where you increased productivity by squeezing the workers so hard they quit in droves and you blamed Human Resources. But again you came out smelling like a rose and went to work for a company you leveraged so far into debt that a five percent increase in market share couldn't make up for it—and you left because of a 'lack of vision.' And now you're in trouble again and blaming it on everybody around you. Did I miss anything?"

"What's your point, Foot?" Phillip asked defiantly.

"Me thinks you're headed for the bottom, shipmate, that's what me thinks," said Long John Foot.

"No way! I can still turn this strut thing around. I haven't hit bottom yet."

"Well... you don't have to hit bottom to change directions, you know."

"What does *that* mean?"

"When you fell off the ship into the water did you wait until you hit bottom before you started swimming toward the surface?"

"No, of course not."

"Well, that's all I'm saying. When you realize you're in

trouble, the sensible thing is to change direction as soon as possible."

"What makes you think I'm in trouble?"

"Because you keep taking shortcuts, taking the easy way out, like cutting prices 'til the merchandise sells itself or improving productivity by squeezing the life out of your people or trying to substitute money for strategy. It's like you don't think you can do it any other way, like you're not good enough. What makes you afraid you can't make it on hard work and sound judgment?"

That thought caught Phillip flat-footed and left him completely befuddled. All he could offer in response was, "What makes you such a wise ass?" But somewhere down in his gut, the idea landed like a brick in a bathtub and sent ripples racing inside him.

Foot just burst out laughing. "Aye, Matey, guilty as charged!" he roared, "Cap'n Wiseass, at your service!"

Phillip frowned and pretended to be absorbed in his fishing. *What does this jerk know about anything?* he thought to himself. *Foot is a grad school dropout. What would he know about working in the corporate world? What would he know about the sacrifices I had to make or the politics involved?*

Phillip had never really excelled, but he never really had to. With money and connections, he had a gilded invitation to the big leagues. Phillip had become a seasoned social and academic ticket puncher, exuding charm and charisma. He could turn it on and turn it off with chilling precision.

Once again, Phillip's mind returned to the painful churning of old memories and the stinging rebuke of his father. After years of these exchanges, he rebounded quickly and with his natural warmth, charm, and newly earned Ivy League pedigree in hand, he landed a plum internship with a prestigious marketing company that would carry him through to his MBA.

Phillip grew to trust his boss, Bill Brewer, who had shown him the ropes and seemed to enjoy referring to Phillip as a testament to his own astute ability to hire well. Phillip reveled in the encouragement and took his coaching to heart. Bill filled a vacuum Donald had created.

Bill liked being known as a developer of people and continually espoused the fact that he groomed his staff to replace him. Yet, it was not his goal to groom them to eclipse him and risk losing his power base within the organization.

So, when Helen McCray, VP of Advertising, suggested Phillip lead a high-visibility project, Bill felt threatened but coolly projected a calculated political line, endorsing her selection. He was capable of playing the game from both angles.

Phillip was proud to be chosen and determined not to let down his revered boss. As the project progressed, Phillip blossomed, gaining the ear of many respected, key individuals in the company and garnering support and dedication from his team.

At Bill's request, Phillip met with him each Friday afternoon to review progress and details. When it came time for Phillip to present the project to key leaders in the company, he and Bill met one last time. Bill coached Phillip to remove several key recommendations the team had made, telling him the ideas wouldn't fly. Although he questioned the request, an eager-to-please Phillip complied.

And then, with a sinking feeling, Phillip recalled the day of his fateful presentation. "Next..." he could still hear the flat voice of Helen McCray. Phillip made his presentation with pride which was soon crushed under the weight of betrayal. It had been so surreal. Once he had made his final statement, the VP questioned his dedication to the project and pointed out that he had missed a number of solutions that should have been included. She scolded him like a child for not seeking the advice of his boss, Bill, who had been brimming with good ideas throughout. Then she began listing some of Bill's good ideas, the ones he had stolen from Phillip and had told him to remove from his presentation.

Phillip was dumbfounded. The shock he felt after his trusted mentor had betrayed him numbed Phillip to his core. "Anything else?" she asked coldly. With no response, she looked over the top of her reading glasses and flatly said, "Next...."

Phillip realized then that his chance for a successful postgraduate career with this company was over. His hard work had become just another feather in Bill's cap. And Phillip had become just another action item in the endless succession of meetings and the corporate chess game of private agendas and politics. "Next...."

Once again, the carrot had been a ruse. He stood frozen at the end of the conference room. He was engulfed in a sea of blank faces—no eye contact, no expression. He was cold, alone, with no help and no idea where to go or what to do. He was shocked that his *so-called team* had stood by, saying nothing, letting him take the fall. And, even more so, he was furious with himself for letting down his guard and trusting Bill. This experience had further poisoned his view. He admonished himself, thinking, *How could I have been so stupid, or so naive?* Later, after returning to the familiar halls of academia to complete his MBA, Phillip vowed he would never let this happen again. And it was at this moment that Phillip was jolted from the past to realize that his fall from the ship wasn't the first time he had plunged into the abyss.

He had dutifully fulfilled his father's manifesto of demands and yet, where had that gotten him? He had paid the price, he had earned his stripes, he thought—and now it was his turn to call the shots.

That's what it took! Phillip thought. *That's what I had to do! And now I deserve some rewards and I shouldn't have to put up with whiners and slackers. What does this jerk know about anything?*

Something that Foot had said nagged at him. Now his own rationalization was an uncomfortable fit. A reluctant Phillip wondered, *Could this guy have a point?*

Just then Foot broke Phillip's melancholic reverie by standing up and stretching loudly, as if it hurt and felt good at the same time. "Aaaaaaaaaaaahhhhhhh!" he bellowed,

"Finally! She's finished, lad, and she's not bad if I do say so myself."

"What?" asked Phillip, "What have you finished? Some kind of awning to keep the sun off?"

"Well," Foot responded thoughtfully, "she might serve that way—but what she is, is a *sail*!"

"A sail??!!" Phillip said with astonishment. "What good is a sail? Maybe you haven't noticed, but we don't have a mast!"

"Have you ever done any wind surfing?" Foot asked with a smile.

"No."

"Well, if this works like I think it will, you're in for a treat. Help me spread it out."

Phillip helped Foot spread out the canvas. It formed an isosceles triangle, about ten feet high and eight feet across. Foot had used fishing line to sew wide hems along both of the long sides. Into each of these hems, he inserted the blade of the oar and tied them together at the top of the handles, forming a large V-shape. About halfway down on each side he cut a hole in the canvas, exposing the oars. Then, leaving a little slack in the canvas, he tied a third oar to the two exposed oar sections, creating a crossbar to stabilize the triangular-shaped sail.

At the bow, they took the tied-together oar handles and shoved them into a slot created by the intersection of the ribs and king plank on the deck. Next Foot crawled underneath the sail, grabbed the cross oar and heaved the sail into an upright position.

Then, with his goofy-foot keeping the handles lodged firmly against the ribs, he began positioning the sail to try to catch the wind. There wasn't much of a breeze but, by moving the sail around until he found just the right angle, Foot got it to fill. Phillip was amazed to feel the boat actually begin to move.

"Yeeeeeeeeee haaaaaaaaaaaaa!!!!!" shouted Foot. "Pull in the sea anchor and the fishing line, take the helm and keep us headed south, Mr. Phelps!"

"Aye, aye, Cap'n!" shouted Phillip with glee. And they set sail. The wind picked up and soon the boat was going fast enough to actually leave a wake. Phillip had to admit that, even if what they were doing was in vain, it felt better to be moving than to just be waiting.

The Fourth Wave

"Water, water, everywhere, nor any drop to drink."

Samuel Taylor Coleridge

Phillip and Foot sailed until sunset, when the wind died, and Foot untied the third oar to collapse the sail. They threw out the anchor, put fishing line over the side and then dined, once again, on peach slices and few meager gulps of water. They were now down to their last bottle.

Completely exhausted, Foot fell asleep with the empty water bottle still in his hand. Phillip wasn't sleepy yet. He watched the sun set in a brilliant display of pinks, reds and purples projected onto a line of languid clouds floating just above the horizon. Phillip had seen sunsets before, through the windows of airplanes and taxis, in between high-rise buildings, and occasionally, through the window of his apartment, but he had never seen anything like this. It was incredible, like sitting on the edge of the world with nothing to block the view.

Phillip watched the stars come out, something else he had never seen before, at least, not like this. It was the same sky he had slept under for the last few nights, of course, but for some reason this was the first time he had ever really *seen* it. Phillip found it every bit as incredible and unreal as the sunset. How could he not have seen this before, he wondered? The stars were so bright! And there were so many! He could see the Milky Way very clearly and he was awed to think of how many stars there must be in the galaxy. It also made him wonder what else he might have failed to notice. For the first time in his life, Phillip felt insignificant.

His thoughts turned inward. *What do I really want? Is my career going forward or backward? Could Foot have a point about my not feeling I'm good enough?* Then, he recalled the painful memories of the previous night, *Could my efforts to live up to my father's expectations still be running my life? Am I still trying to check off the boxes on someone else's list? Or am I trying to get even for what I had to give up?* He wondered, *Could I be sabotaging myself? Is that what Foot meant when he said I threw myself overboard?* As the boat rocked in the moonlight, these questions haunted Phillip. But soon fatigue overpowered him and he, too, fell asleep.

The next morning, Phillip was the first one awake. Foot was in the same position in which he had fallen asleep, the empty water bottle in hand. Phillip said, "Wake up, Foot!" There was no response. He shouted. Still no response. So he leaned over and shook Foot vigorously. That did the trick, but Foot had a tough time waking. He started to sit up, but only groaned and lay back. Then he took in a deep breath and sat up with a grimace.

"What's wrong, Foot?"

"It turns out that wind surfing uses different muscles than regular surfing—and right now, they're all screaming at me."

Foot closed his eyes, drew in another deep breath and exhaled slowly as he moved his outstretched arms in a graceful circle. As he completed the circle, he opened his eyes and said, "What's for breakfast?"

Phillip turned to pick up his fishing shoe. "Whatever's on the end of my...." He had checked the bait last night just before it got dark and swore he had gone to sleep with the shoe in his hand, but now he didn't see it. He looked on both sides of the bench he had slept on. He looked under the extra canvas. But the Gucci was gone.

"It's gone," he said through clenched teeth.

"What's gone?" asked Foot at the end of his next inhale.

"My shoe," Phillip said slowly and distinctly.

"Your shoe?" responded Foot, drawing in another breath and

beginning another graceful Tai Chi movement.

"Yeah, the one I was fishing with. It's gone—hook, line and sinker, you might say," Phillip said bitterly.

"Musta been a fish," said Foot as he turned to get more line and tackle.

"I had a lot on my mind last night," Phillip said defensively.

"Here," said Foot, handing the line and tackle to Phillip "There's not enough wind to sail right now, so throw out another one."

"I can't believe I was so stupid!" said Phillip with surprising anger.

"Forget about it. It could happen to anybody," Foot said in a soothing manner, as he stood up and cocked one arm back, thrust the other forward and slowly turned in a half-circle.

"No. It was a stupid mistake and there's no excuse for it," Phillip insisted.

"You're being pretty hard on yourself," Foot said with his eyes closed. "You that hard on your people?"

"Look," Phillip burst out, "sometimes you have to be hard on yourself, you have to expect more! There's no room for mistakes, no room to fail," Phillip said with the same passion of his father before him. "If other people can't cut it—don't get it—good riddance—I'm not a social worker, I'm a businessman—they need to go work for somebody else!" Phillip's sudden rise of emotion startled even himself. He had become a walking replica of everything he had vowed never to become.

Foot reversed his stance and stretched in the opposite direction. "Sounds like that must have been some of what you had on your mind last night."

"Here's the bottom line," Phillip said more rationally, "I made a mistake that cost us our breakfast. I don't make mistakes or tolerate them. There's no excuse for it, and I won't let it happen again. I'll tie it off this time."

"No!" exclaimed Foot without interrupting his Tai Chi. "A fishing line has to give when a fish hits it, that's why they do it with flexible poles. If a fish hits a line with no give, he'll snap it off like it was made of glass. We don't have a pole, but your arm serves the same purpose. It puts 'give' in the system. If you're going to be a leader, you've got to know all about 'give.'"

By now Phillip was beginning to value Foot's opinion. "What do you mean?" he asked, as he wrapped the fishing line around his remaining Gucci.

Shifting to another position, Foot replied, "When you're a leader, what you give is what you get."

"How's that?" asked Phillip genuinely.

"Ninety-nine times out of one-hundred, what happens when you give somebody a smile?" Foot queried.

"They usually smile back," answered Phillip.

"Yup," responded Foot while slowly raising one leg in the air. "You give the people who work for you respect and you get back respect in return, just like a smile. You give them responsibility, they act responsibly. You do your best for them, they do their best for you. You give them the flexibility to be human, and they don't snap off your line and leave you hungry."

Phillip thought about that as he baited the hook and threw it out. "Where'd you learn so much about being a leader?" he asked.

"I've sailed with a lot of different captains, some good, some bad, some with crews who would go to the bottom with them, some with crews in a virtual state of mutiny, and I learned from both kinds," Foot said reflectively. Then he dropped into his Long John Silver persona. "Kind 'o makes ye think, don't it? Which one might *you* be?"

Before Phillip could answer, a stiff breeze blew up out of the east and Foot shouted, "Surf's up!" Then he set to work tying the third oar back in place. This time Foot also tied one end of a piece of rope to the handles of the sail and the other end to one of the benches.

"What's that for?" Phillip inquired.

"Yesterday, this puppy almost got away from me a couple of times," Foot said, "and I don't want to lose it if that happens for real, you know?"

And with that, Foot hoisted the sail into place, Phillip drew in the anchor and the fishing line, manned the helm and they were under way.

"Steer us a few degrees to the west of magnetic south," Foot shouted over his shoulder as wind filled the sail.

Phillip looked down at the compass built into the helm. "Why?" he shouted back, "I thought south was where we wanted to go."

"We want to go *true* south," Foot replied. "That's the shortest route to the shipping lanes. But the compass points to magnetic south, which is north of Antarctica and west of South America and would pull us off to the east. So we compensate by steering a few degrees west. Things aren't always what they seem, you know?"

"You should be right at home with that!" Phillip said openly.

"With what?" Foot asked.

"With things that aren't what they seem!" Phillip said with a nod toward Foot.

They sailed for quite awhile, with a steady easterly wind and a straight course true south. But when the wind started to shift, Foot took a break. Crawling out from under the laid-down sail, Foot stood up stiffly and said, "Your turn."

This was something Phillip had never considered. Foot was the one who knew how to surf. He had just assumed that Foot would do it. "What do you mean 'my turn'? I don't know how to sail!"

"Neither did I, before yesterday," said Foot. "You'll get the hang of it. I have to give my back some slack. It's cramping up something fierce. Crawl under and hoist her up. You've seen how I do it."

Foot moved to the helm and Phillip started to hoist the sail into position—but a gust of wind grabbed it before it was completely up and Phillip found himself hanging on to what was now a hang glider threatening to lift him off the boat. Then the wind dropped and so did the sail forcing Phillip to start again.

This time, Phillip waited in the bottom of the boat for a break in the wind and he lifted the sail quickly. He shoved the handles into the bow and brought the sail upright, holding it parallel to the wind to keep it from filling before he was ready. When he felt stable with it, he turned it slowly into the wind. Then it filled with a 'pop'—and almost pulled him overboard

Phillip had to collapse his weight-bearing leg and bring the sail down on top of himself once again. "How's that back doing, Foot?" he shouted from under the canvas. "All better?"

"Don't be impudent, ye scurvy son of a sea hag! Hoist the mains'l! Haul in the bow line!" commanded Long John Foot.

So, Phillip repeated his actions, but this time he braced himself before turning the sail into the wind. And this time he fared better. The sail filled. Phillip leaned back to balance its pull and he could feel it beginning to move the boat. But in a matter of seconds, the sail went slack and no matter how he moved it, he couldn't find the right spot again. The sail would pop out, then start to flutter. He would move it and it would pop out again. He tried moving it forward, backward, right and left, but he couldn't keep it in the sweet spot no matter how much strength he applied. He began to get irritated. And Foot's steady laughter didn't help.

"This wind is no good, Foot!" Phillip shouted over his shoulder. "Maybe we should wait for a better wind!"

"You're fighting it!" Foot shouted. "And it's fighting you because you're trying to control it! Try just guiding it! It's all about balance!"

"Yeah, right," thought Phillip. "Next he'll be telling me to become one with the wind."

Phillip tried again...and again...and again. He felt sure that if he only could find the right spot and then keep the cursed thing from wobbling, he would have it. He even tried shoving the handles into the bow with both feet to keep it still. But nothing worked.

As he crawled out from under the collapsed sail for the fifth time, Foot said, "Look," then he leaned over the side of the boat, scooped some water into his hand and showed it to Phillip. "It's like holding water in your hand," he said. "The only way you can do it is to hold it in an open hand, because," now Foot slowly closed his fist, "the harder you try to grasp it, the more quickly it flows away." And the water ran out between his fingers.

Phillip tried again, gingerly, with an open hand, being all about balance and...he kept the sail filled for a good two minutes before he lost it! Foot was right. The secret lay in guiding it, not controlling it. The next time Phillip kept it filled for five minutes, then for ten. Now he was wind surfing, reacting without thought, responding to the wind like he w*as* one with the wind. This was the most exhilarating experience of his life.

They took a break at midday, as the sun burned directly overhead, for Foot to take a sextant reading. He found that even though they *were* making measurable progress, they were still, distressingly, too many miles away from the shipping lanes. Even so, he suggested that they break for an hour or so. But Phillip was as eager to get back to wind surfing like a kid with a new toy. That afternoon they took turns manning the sail until the wind died away at sunset, and they folded it up for the night.

They ate their peaches and drank their small cup of water that evening in reverent silence. The sunset was *that* beautiful.

After dinner, Phillip baited his hook and threw out his line, this time with the line tied to a strip of canvas around his wrist, and then he settled back to watch the stars come out.

After wrestling the sail all day, Phillip's muscles ached. His sun-scorched skin pulled tight around his knees. His blistered lips throbbed as they cracked a little deeper. Phillip was tired, but he thought, it was a good tired. He remembered the last time he had felt that way, the last time he felt so tired yet had felt such a deep sense of accomplishment. A hint of a smile tugged at his now deeply burned face as he remembered working with his team on a Habitat house.

When Phillip felt waves of fatigue starting to close over him, he welcomed them. He fell asleep marveling at how alive he felt—and how ironic it was that they might die.

The Fifth Wave

"…the fish is my friend…I must kill him.
I'm glad we do not have to kill the stars."

Ernest Hemingway

The next morning, Phillip was awakened just before dawn by the sensation of hot, barbed wire being threaded through his back. It felt as though every muscle he had was on fire and now some demon was poking at them with a sharp stick. To make matters worse, his head felt thick and heavy and he couldn't figure out what was happening. Then the fog cleared just enough for him to realize that his pain was being caused by something tugging at his arm. What, he wondered, could possibly be... A FISH!

Through a flash of searing pain, Phillip bolted upright, the thought of food drowning out all other sensations. In the gray, predawn light he could just make out the scraps of canvas he used for gloves. He grabbed them with his free hand and began drawing the fish in hand over hand as before. "Foot!" he shouted, "Foot! Wake up! I've got one! I need your help!" Foot did not stir.

Phillip looked around for the knife but didn't see it. The fish was almost at the boat. He could just make it out under the surface, a flat, vertical kind of fish. He knew that trying to bring it on board without a gaff or net was risky, but now he had no choice. With a slow, even hand, he pulled the fish out of the water and actually got it over the boat before it flipped off the hook—and landed right on Foot's sleeping face.

"Arrrrrrrrgggggggggg!" shouted Foot, with his hands flailing all around his head. Then the fish flipped off his face and Foot sat up with a gasp. "What the—" he started, until he saw the fish at his feet. "Breakfast!" he shouted, then moaned in pain as he bent to pick it up. Holding up a small wahoo, Foot said with a grin, "I dreamed I was being born and the doctor just kept slapping me and slapping me!" They both laughed until their sore backs made them stop.

"It worked!" Phillip marveled, as Foot went to work on the fish. "It all worked! It really worked!"

"What?" Foot asked without looking up.

"The canvas wrist strap, the arm, the 'give.' It all worked just like you said it would. No snapped-off line."

"Yup," said Foot quietly, as he pulled off a filet and handed it to Phillip. "Here. I'll let you roll it up yourself this time." Then Foot pulled off the other fillet and flung the fish's head and guts as far out to sea as he could.

They ate like ravenous wolves, scarfing down the big fillets like they were sardines. They ate so fast that they had to wait for the sensation—that head-clearing, mind-calming, and invigorating warmth that spread from their stomachs outward. And when it came, they both sighed with relief, knowing they would live another day, as sore and painful as it promised to be.

There wasn't any wind yet, so Phillip and Foot just sat and watched the sun come up in a spectacular display of red and gold. Phillip was awestruck. "Just when I think I've seen the most beautiful sky, I see something even more breathtaking." But Foot just sat there, looking at the sky pensively. "I guess when you've seen sunrises like that a thousand times, they don't impress you much anymore, huh, Foot?"

"No, it's not that," Foot said thoughtfully.

"Then what? You too sore to be impressed today?"

"It's nothing. Red sky in the morning, sailors take warning.[5] Just an old sailor's superstition. Sometimes it means something, sometimes it doesn't."

"Well it looks like a gorgeous day to me," said Phillip

cheerfully. Then he stood with a groan to stretch his tortured muscles—and his pants fell to his feet.

"Welcome to Cap'n Wiseass's seagoing spa and weight-loss center," Foot said with a laugh. "Results guaranteed!" And again, they both laughed until the pain made them stop.

When the laughter and pain subsided, Phillip looked out over a sea as flat as a dinner plate. "Looks like we're going no place in a hurry this morning," he said.

"Yeah," Foot responded, "but when the wind does pick up, we have a decision to make."

"What's that?" inquired Phillip.

"Well, from this latitude, I can see that the swells from the island are running at more of an angle to the big ones. That means it's farther to the west of us than I thought. Until now, we've been going for both the island and the sea lanes, but now we have to decide between them. If we stay with a southerly heading, we'll reach the shipping lanes one or two days earlier. But there's no guarantee we'll see a ship. If we head for the island, it'll take longer to reach the shipping lanes *or* the island—and even if we reach the island, there's no guarantee we'll find any food or water," Foot said thoughtfully.

"And we've only got one can of peaches and a half liter of water left," Phillip added. "What are we going to do?"

Foot just stared out over the sea for several minutes, and then he said matter-of-factly, "My gut tells me to go directly for the shipping lanes."

Phillip waited for further explanation, but there was none. "So that's it then? Your gut says 'shipping lanes' and so it's 'shipping lanes'? That's all there is to it?" he asked anxiously.

"Yup," said Foot. "You could go back and forth in your head all day about the risks versus the odds versus the time versus the chances of this and that, but there's no solid answer there. So sometimes you just have to shut down your head and listen to your gut—and this is one of those times."

"Seems like a big decision to be made on nothing but intuitive 'feelings'," Phillip worried.

"Hey," said Foot, "your gut usually knows more than your head about what you *should* be doing. For example, can you honestly tell me that you didn't have a gut feeling that you were alienating the people who work for you?"

"Maybe," said Phillip, "but I don't operate on 'feelings.' So what?"

"So, maybe you should have listened to your gut. Maybe if you had, somebody might be coming to your rescue right now, literally *and* figuratively," Foot said reproachfully. "But, as it is, what do you think your people will do when they get back and find out what's going on? Do you think they'll try to cover for you and fix the problem? Or, do you think they'll do everything they can to ensure that they get a new boss out of the deal?"

Phillip could only bite his lip. "Ok," he said defensively, "let's assume, just for the sake of argument, that people skills have not been my strongest suit." Then Phillip added sarcastically, "What does your vast experience have to offer in way of advice for that?"

"Not much, really," Foot replied, "just the Golden Rule."[6]

"The Golden Rule. That's it?" said Phillip skeptically.

"What more do you need?" Foot responded. "Of course you have to realize that 'do unto others as you would have them do unto you' means 'do unto you' if you *were* them, *not* if you were in their position. It means you really have to *know* them, what their hopes, fears, and self-interests are—because a real leader doesn't try to make people surrender their own interests in favor of his or the company's. He brings all their differing self-interests into concert and makes an orchestra out of a discordant mob. He knows whom to encourage and whom to challenge, when to praise publicly and when to critique privately. He offers different incentives to different people depending on their individual needs and interests. And, he knows that the relationship between productivity and morale means that *everybody* needs to have input, a chance to make a real contribution, and the assurance of real recognition. At least that's the way it seems to me. How does it seem to you?"

"Well..." Phillip admitted slowly, "maybe I have tended to project what I would do in a given situation and then expect others to be like me."

"How's that working out?" asked a thoughtful Foot.

"I just never thought about it like that, I guess," Phillip said without answering the question. Then, he said, somewhat cynically, "I guess it's the Golden Rule with a twist. Why am I not surprised? Sounds like it might be Foot's Rule to me." Then he brightened and said, "Hey! I feel a breeze!"

"So you do!" verified Foot. "We can set sail in a few minutes. But in the meantime, I want to wash off this face full of fish and get a little refreshment thing going here. How about a quick swim?"

Phillip needed no encouragement. With his pants already down, he quickly ripped off his shirt and shouted, "Last one in's a rotten egg!" with the joy of a child.

Down the boat and over the stern he went, not bothering with the ladder attached to it, Foot following right behind. The cool and bracing water felt even better than they had anticipated. As they watched the sun dance on the water, the breeze started to pick up. For a time, it was actually possible to put their situation out of mind and just enjoy the invigorating sensations. Abruptly, Foot broke the mood .

"Get back in the boat," he said with authority.

"Why?" asked Phillip. "What's wrong?"

"Probably nothing. Just get back in the boat. NOW!" said Foot harshly.

Then Phillip saw the fin and felt his heart leap out of his chest. It cut the water about ten yards away and it was heading right for them. Though Foot was closer, Phillip lunged for the ladder and was there in two strokes. He grabbed it at the same time Foot did and scrambled up with a push from Foot. Then he turned to help Foot—just in time to see his head yanked violently under the water. Foot had hold of the ladder with both hands, his knuckles turning white. Phillip watched in horror as he was engulfed in a roiling sea of red.

In a panic, Phillip glanced around for something, anything, to…he didn't know what. Foot's head popped back up, he gasped loudly for air, then he was yanked back down again. Not knowing what else to do, Phillip reached down and grabbed Foot by the hair and pulled. He could see and feel the jolt of the shark pulling against him, a nine-foot tiger thrashing violently from side to side. He felt it suddenly let go.

In an instant, Foot was yanked up the ladder and into the boat. "How badly are you hurt?" Phillip shouted—then he saw. Foot's right leg was gone from mid-calf down—and it wasn't a tidy amputation. Bone, blood vessels, and muscle tissue were all hanging out the ragged end and one blood vessel was pumping out blood in huge spurts.

"He got my leg," said Foot with surprising calm. "I need something to make a tourniquet."

Phillip couldn't move. His head was suddenly spinning and so was his stomach. His knees became rubbery. All he could do was sit down before he fell down.

"Easy now," Foot coached with astounding evenness. "Take slow, deep breaths. Don't pass out on me. I need you. I need to get a tourniquet on this as soon as possible."

Foot's calm gave Phillip unusual resolve. Phillip pulled out of his swoon and he found a piece of rope. Handing it to Foot, Phillip asked with amazement, "How can you be so calm?"

"Because I'm all full of adrenaline and endorphins right now. I don't feel a thing. That's not going to last long," Foot said as he wrapped the rope tightly just below his knee. "I've seen this kind of thing before. I'll be going into shock soon and we need to tie off this spurter before I do, because this tourniquet isn't going to last long either."

"How do we do that?" Phillip asked in a panic.

Foot thought for a moment, then said, "The fishing line."

"What?" asked a confused Phillip.

"The fishing line," Foot insisted, starting to look a little pale. "Use some fishing line to tie it off."

"Oh!" Phillip responded. "OK!" He reached over, grabbed the line, and stood with it in his hand staring at Foot's severed leg.

"Don't go wobbly on me," Foot encouraged him. "just tie it off. It's the one spouting all the blood," he said with a weak laugh. Now Foot was definitely looking pale, and his voice grew thin and strained. "And when you're done, I may need a blanket," he said weakly.

Phillip shook his head to snap himself out of his inaction,

then clenched his jaw and set about the grim task. The pumping artery was easy to see. It was right at the surface of the torn flesh, close to a splintered bone, but it was slippery. It took three tries using the fine fishing line to get the artery tied off. When it was, Foot let go of the rope and fell back with a moan. The line held and the flow of blood diminished to a slow drip.

Phillip carefully trimmed the extra line with the Swiss Army knife and bandaged Foot's stump as best he could with his tux shirt, then wrapped him as tightly as he could in the blanket. He made a sun shade for Foot's head out of a fold of canvas, then sat back to catch his breath. His mind was racing. *It should have been me,* he thought, *Foot was closer to the boat. He should have been the first one in. And it's my fault we're here in the first place. But he pushed me back in the boat first!*

Even though Foot's eyes were starting to close now, Phillip had to ask. "Foot, why did you let me get in the boat first? You were closer. Why did you push me in first?"

Foot opened his eyes and replied weakly, "Because I'm the captain—or at least I was at that point in time—and a captain's first duty is to the safety of his passengers and crew."

"What do you mean you were 'at that time'?" Phillip asked.

"I mean when the captain becomes unable to carry out his duties, the first mate has to take over. So I'm promotin' you to Cap'n, Matey. Now it's your duty," Foot said with a forced smile. Then Foot closed his eyes and lost consciousness.

For awhile, all Phillip could do was sit there in despair and recrimination. Then he asked himself what Foot would do if the situation were reversed and he knew he had to take action. He knew he had to get Foot some medical help as fast as possible. And his gut told him to follow Foot's instincts and sail south.

Phillip made Foot as comfortable as he could, then he tied the third oar onto the sail and prepared it for hoisting. He checked the helm and found that they were still pointing a few degrees west of south. He tied the rudder in place with a piece of rope. Now, Phillip faced a new dilemma.

Phillip knew that without Foot to spell him, he wasn't going to be able to sail for long, not with his back tied in knots the way it was. He also knew, though, that he had to. Just going for it wasn't going to work for long. Phillip knew he could *not* fail. Foot's life was at stake, never mind his own. There had to be a way, there *had* to…then he had an idea.

Phillip used the Swiss Army knife to cut two lengths of rope, and then crawled under the sail. He tied one end of each piece to bench struts on either side of the boat, thinking as he did so, *I sure hope these struts hold.* Then he took the other ends and passed each through one of the openings in the canvas hems holding the vertical oars. He passed the rope around behind the hemmed oar and out over the third, horizontal oar. Holding both loose ends of the rope in his left hand, he grabbed the third oar with his right hand and heaved the sail into place.

He held an end of the rope in each hand, and using them like reins, he turned the sail to catch the wind. The ropes nearly leapt from his hands when the canvas popped. "It worked," he yelled, "It worked!" The ropes now took the forward force of the sail and held it back. He found that the ropes not only took the strain his back had previously taken, but that the sail was far more stable this way. Adjustments were easier to make, too, just by shortening one rope and letting out the other. When the wind shifted, he was even able to move the sail over with less strain than before.

Phillip was able to sail, more or less, all day like that. When evening came and the wind died down, he was extremely grateful for the break. He untied the third oar, stowed the sail, and checked on Foot.

Foot's eyes were still closed, but his color was better, so Phillip spoke to him. "You awake, Foot?"

"Hard to tell," came the answer. "I keep slipping in and out."

"Well at least you're not *staying* out," said Phillip with relief. "How's the leg?"

"It's weird," replied Foot. "It really feels like it's still there, just like they say—and it hurts!"

Phillip turned away quickly, fighting back his tears and went about opening the last can of peaches to pull himself together. He insisted that Foot eat the peaches, saying Foot needed the nourishment more than he did. Foot refused. So Phillip insisted, as captain, that Foot drink all the peach juice. Again, Foot refused. "Passenger's prerogative," he said. So they split the juice—and the last of the water.

Then Phillip threw out the anchor, baited the hook, threw out the line, slipped on the canvas wrist strap and fell dead asleep.

The Sixth Wave

"The world breaks everyone, and afterward, some are strong at the broken places. But those that will not break, it kills."

Ernest Hemingway

The next day dawned dark. The sky was overcast and a gusty wind was blowing. There was also the smell of rain.

Phillip awoke to find Foot already awake, sitting at the helm and looking ten years older. Foot's face was strained and his dehydrated skin showed wrinkles far more deeply. "I'm glad to see you up—but you don't look so good," Phillip said.

"How do you feel?"

Foot looked over at Phillip's sunburned face with its cracked lips and scraggly five-day beard. "You're not going to win any prizes, either," Foot said. "And how I feel is *stupid*."

"Stupid!!? Why!?" exclaimed Phillip. "I know you don't believe in accidents, but even *you* have to admit that sometimes—"

"I knew when I threw the fish guts overboard that they might draw a shark. That's why I threw them as far as I could. Then I forgot about it. *That* was the stupid part. When I threw the fish guts, I threw a stone in the water—and this," Foot said nodding to his missing foot, "is one of its ripples. Now I just have to figure out why I did that. I must need a change."

Phillip was speechless. He would have been thinking about who he was going to sue if he were in Foot's place. "That's why you threw yourself overboard, you know," Foot said. "You knew in your gut that you needed to change and just didn't know how else to make it happen."

Phillip wasn't going to argue with a man who had just lost part of his leg, especially one who just might be right. Instead, he just said, "You're a remarkable guy, Foot."

Foot ignored the compliment. "I don't suppose there's anything on the other end of that line tied to your wrist, is there?" he asked.

Phillip gave the line a tug. "No," he said. "Nothing."

"Well, then, begging the cap'n's pardon, sir, but you've got a great big old hairy decision to make."

"What's that?"

"Whether to ride the wave we've got or wait for a better one."

"Sorry, Foot. I'm going to need a little more than that to go on."

"Well, it's kinda like this," Foot responded. "It's like I was telling you about waves and how they come in sets of seven."

"Yeah?" Phillip prodded.

"Well, the seventh wave is thought to be the best. According to lore, it's the biggest and most powerful of the seven, and it'll usually give you the best ride. So you're out there on your board and you're waiting for a good wave. Each time one comes, you have to make the decision, whether this is the one you're going to ride or whether you're going to hold out for the seventh."

"But then," Foot continued, "it's not always as simple a decision as it might seem, because maybe you're getting hungry or maybe it's getting dark or maybe there are a dozen other hot dogs out there waiting for the same wave, and you don't like surfing in a crowd. There is a whole list of reasons that might make picking another wave a better decision."

"Ok," Phillip interjected, "so…?"

"So the sailors' warning we saw yesterday morning was a

true one," Foot warned. "We're in for a blow. I have no idea how bad it's going to get, but I know it's not exactly going to be the 'seventh wave' of wind surfing. It'll certainly blow up waves big enough to swamp us if we get crosswise to them even once, so we have to stay headed into the waves at all times."

"So what's the big hairy decision?" Phillip asked nervously as he looked out toward the rapidly approaching storm.

"*Your* decision," Foot corrected, "is this: There are two ways to stay headed into the waves. One way is to throw out the sea anchor and try to ride the storm out where we are. The other way..." Foot paused and bit his lip slightly, "is to *sail* with them and that way is riskier because the wind will be gusting all over the place and the sail will be hard to control—and all I'll be able to do is man the helm and maybe work the foot pedal on the bilge pump with my good leg. We could end up scuttled or dead from exhaustion. BUT..." he paused, "...the same wind that might send us to the bottom, might also take us a long way toward the shipping lanes."

Both of them sat in silence, feeling the increasing wind, smelling the coming rain, and watching the growing whitecaps.

"We might save as much as a day," Foot offered reflectively, "and there's a slim chance it might take us all the way—or it could shred the sail and capsize us." Then he looked directly at Phillip. "So the decision is, Cap'n...do we ride *this* wave or wait for a better one?"

Phillip responded without thinking. For once, he gave no

thought to strategy, tactics, or perception; to how he might be perceived, the results he wanted, or the wording that would provide the best cover in case of accountability. He just immediately blurted out straight from his gut, "WE RIDE!"

Foot smiled through his pain and said, "Spoken like a true leader."

"Really, Foot, we can do it," said Phillip enthusiastically. "You didn't see yesterday, but I rigged a way to…"

"I *did* see," interrupted Foot, "otherwise, I never would have even *mentioned* trying to ride the storm. What you did was brilliant—and it worked. I was conscious enough to see that. You adapted to change and turned a seemingly impossible situation into a victory. You must have covered a lot of ocean yesterday. Now, you may just save our bacon. Pretty impressive accomplishments for an MBA. And you know what?"

"What?"

"You did it with hard work and sound judgment. Maybe you do have what it takes after all. Whaddayathink?"

But Philip didn't know *what* to think. He felt his face flush and he turned away. For the first time, he had the chance to take a bow and he was speechless. All he could muster was, "Let's do it!"

Phillip leapt into action and started preparing the sail but Foot stopped him by saying, "Beggin' the cap'n's pardon again, sir, but don't you want to batten down the hatches first?"

"Oh! Yeah, sure," said Phillip as he started gathering up the empty cans and bottles and anything loose he could find. "But you can stow that 'cap'n' stuff where the sun don't shine, 'shipmate,' because we're in this *together*. You're going to depend on me and I'm going to depend on you. *Right*?"

"Sounds like the basis of a mighty sound policy to me, Cap'n!" Foot chimed in as cheerfully as he could.

"Stop that!" Phillip insisted. "We're in the *same boat*, Foot! Ever heard that one before?"

"By all the saints at sea, I do believe you have promise, shipmate," said Foot hoarsely. "Would that I might have lived to see you fulfill it!"

"You're going to live, Foot!" shouted Phillip over his shoulder as he removed two life vests from their forward compartment and stowed everything else, except the left-over canvas, in its place. "Here, put this on," he said, handing Foot a life vest.

"Aye, aye, Cap'n!" Foot retorted.

"Am I going to have to slap you?" shouted Phillip as he tucked the canvas up under the bow. "I'm not above slapping the disabled, you know!"

"That's the spirit!" Foot shouted back.

"I got your 'spirit' right here!" Phillip bantered back as he moved to the sail.

"What does that mean?" Foot asked.

"I have no idea!" Phillip shouted, then drew himself up fully erect and announced, "Stores stowed, Mr. Foot?"

"Aye, aye, Cap'n!" Foot responded .

"Life jackets secured?"

"Aye! Aye!"

Then Phillip turned and looked Foot directly in the eyes and said, very seriously, "Are you OK, Foot? You ready for this?"

"I am, Phillip," replied Foot, "but there's one thing I have to say first."

"What's that?" Phillip said, leaning closer.

"If we should end up in the drink today, you must swim as far away from me as you possibly can," Foot said with deadly sincerity. "You understand?"

At first Phillip couldn't understand why Foot would say that.

Then, he did.

Phillip swallowed hard and quietly said, "I understand."

Now Phillip's mind was flooded with things he wanted to say to Foot, things he *must* say. Foot had said so much that had really made Phillip think. He had saved Phillip's life. They had been through so much together...but now was not the time. *Just another reason to make it through this,* Phillip promised himself.

And all he said was, "Let's ride."

As Foot pulled in the anchor, Phillip disappeared under the sail and when the wind gusts gave him a break he heaved it into position. Phillip was a pro at this now, feeling the wind, turning the sail and tightening his guy ropes all at the same time. The wind took the sail as a challenge and filled it with a vengeance. In the blink of an eye, they were smashing through the chop and leaving a wake.

Phillip felt incomprehensibly good. Dehydrated and malnourished as he was, he felt strong and confident. His head was spinning with all that might happen, all of it bad. He was afraid and rationally should be. How strong would the wind get? Could the waves become even fiercer? How much rain would there be? Would the bilge pump be enough? But his gut said, *You can do this.*

So he turned off his head and went with his gut. And it felt *good.* His muscle aches were gone, banished by adrenaline and determination. One part of Phillip's mind was aware of this and marveled at it. Another part wondered whether it might be possible to run out of adrenaline. Phillip was aware of all these things at once...and was at peace with all of them. *You can't think and surf at the same time,* he told himself.

As the wind grew steadily stronger, the sky steadily darker, and the swells steadily higher, Phillip lost himself in his work, feeling the wind, anticipating its moves, balancing on the crest of its growing power. Sailing across the edge of the storm, they made steady progress into the afternoon. Then the rain started.

It was light rain at first, and it was welcomed. Both Phillip and Foot had their faces turned upward and opened their mouths to take in as much as they could. When the force of the rain grew too hard for that, they were able to get all they wanted just by licking the runoff from their faces.

The sky grew black and lightning split it from every direction. The thunder threatened to deafen them, but Foot and Phillip each managed to stoically maintain his function: Phillip by losing himself in the wind, Foot by reciting a Hemingway passage from *Old Man and the Sea* that helped him keep himself mindful and centered, "...man is not made for defeat. A man can be destroyed but not defeated."[7] Foot knew it wouldn't be long before he would have to start working the foot pump and he knew that would be painful.

There was no doubt that they were making good time, though. This was definitely the fastest they had gone. The waves were up to three or four feet with white caps at the crests, but the boat was riding them with ease, climbing up the front sides and sliding down the back sides at about a thirty-degree angle to the waves.

Foot knew that if the boat took on too much water, she would start to wallow and that could cause them to capsize. He began the painful process of positioning himself so he could steer and work the foot pedal at the same time. The helm was at the rear of the boat on the starboard side, with a bench about two feet from the stern. It was in that space that the bilge pump was located. It was electric, of course, but it could also be operated by foot pedal.

By straddling the bench facing the port side, Foot could operate the foot pump with his left foot and steer with his right hand—for awhile, anyway. The pain was excruciating until Foot found the best way to steady himself on the bench without bumping his stump and sending lightning bolts up his thigh. It was definitely time to start pumping. Water was already two inches deep in the bottom of the boat.

Soon the sea was at five or six feet, big enough to roll the boat over if they attacked a wave at too much of an angle. That made Foot's job tricky. If they sailed straight into the waves, it would take them way off course. If he sailed too much off that path, they would capsize. What Foot had to do was to maintain just the right balance between these two opposing forces, surfing them, just like he always did.

Up front, the rising and falling of the bow was requiring more and more balance from Phillip. He could still see the horizon from the bottom of each trough, but it was way above his head. And when they started down the backside, it felt more and more like Phillip would be pitched over the bow.

But there was no turning back now. And somehow, that thought brought Phillip a strange comfort. Somehow, knowing there was no other choice but to go forward took the anguish out of not knowing how it would end up—and that gave him strength.

Then the storm hit them with everything it had. It grew so dark that Foot could barely see Phillip through the rain. He had to steer the boat more by feel than by sight. He could no longer tell how high the waves were, although he knew that they were big. His right leg was on fire and his left leg was pumping as fast as it could go, but he was losing the race. The water level inside the boat was inching up the sides.

Up front, Phillip felt like he was on a roller coaster, rising straight up then slamming straight down. No horizon was visible now, only water, mountains of water—and *power,* awesome, overwhelming power, all around. Phillip had to add his full weight and strength to the guy ropes to keep the sail in place. Then it happened.

The strain became too much for the sail and it started to split at one of the seams. In the darkness, Phillip didn't notice until the flap hit him in the face. "The sail is coming apart!" he shouted over his shoulder. "What do you recommend now, Mr. Foot?"

"Lay her down before we lose her," Foot shouted over the wind.

Phillip laid the sail down and crawled out. "Now what?" he shouted.

"Get the empty cans out of the forward compartment and start bailing!" yelled Foot, as the boat became almost vertical.

Phillip did as Foot said and brought out three cans as the boat leveled off. "Take over the pump," shouted Foot, "and give me two of the cans!"

Then they started bailing for their lives, but the waves were so high now that they could only bail when the boat was in a trough or climbing the face of the wave. On the downside, the bilge water washed into the bow and threatened to take them under each time it did. When it sloshed back, they bailed like men possessed. It was all they could do. They were fighting for their lives in a nightmare of angry water—and there was no way to wake up.

The Seventh Wave

"Every man's life ends the same way. It is only the details of how he lived and how he died that distinguish one man from another."

Ernest Hemingway

Phillip and Foot were beyond tired, beyond sore, beyond exhausted. Now, they operated on momentum alone, bailing with all their strength on the upsides and catching their breath on the downsides. Still, they were losing. The water was rising.

Phillip suddenly became very aware of his mortality and

something told him that if he were going to say to Foot the things he wanted to say, he had better do it now. So on the next downside, Phillip yelled above the wind, "Foot! There's something I *have* to say!"

And as soon as he did, the rain began to lessen and the wind began to subside. As quickly as it had come, the storm was leaving. In less than a minute, the rain had stopped and the sea began to calm down—and Phillip and Foot suddenly felt very tired, too tired to cheer or celebrate or even say, "Yea!" All Foot could manage was, "Why didn't you do that sooner?" But Phillip was just too tired to laugh. And out on the western horizon, the clouds broke, just in time for the setting sun to ignite the entire sky, illuminating the horizon in Technicolor splendor. But there was no one awake to see it.

The night was mercifully calm, though Phillip and Foot probably would have slept through another storm. The sun was already high and hot by the time Phillip woke up...and it wasn't easy. He couldn't move without pain. His eyes were so crusted over that he couldn't open them right away and when he did, they wouldn't focus for the longest time. Though he was no longer dehydrated, he felt more dead than alive. Then he thought about how Foot must feel and found the strength to sit up.

Foot was exactly where he had fallen the night before, sprawled across the helm bench, face down, the end of his torn leg resting in filthy bilge water. With enormous effort,

Phillip pulled and pushed himself up and went to Foot's aid. He lifted the leg as gently as he could up onto the bench, but the pain of the movement woke Foot.

Foot moaned, opened his eyes about halfway and tried to push himself up, but he collapsed back onto the bench with a groan. Phillip tried to speak to him, only his mouth wouldn't work. He moved his jaw around a bit and was amazed to find even those muscles were sore. When he could finally speak, he managed a mere, "How you doin,' Foot?"

Foot, too, had trouble speaking at first but finally managed to say, "Help me up."

Moving very slowly and painfully, Phillip positioned himself beside Foot and lifted his right leg off the bench a little, then grabbed Foot's left arm and pulled him upright. They both had to rest for a moment afterward. Finally, Foot looked over at Phillip and faintly said, "What's for breakfast?"

They both tried their best to laugh at that. What came out was a pitiful series of coughs, wheezes, and groans instead. Phillip looked at Foot with a crooked smile and said, "You look like you could use a drink." And in their demented mental state, they even found *that* hilarious and issued another round of laugh-groans.

Though the sun was hot, there was a good breeze and the day was pleasant. "Any chance you can sail?" Foot asked.

"Don't make me laugh any more!" Phillip replied, "It hurts too much. I don't even think I've got enough strength to mend the sail."

Foot sympathetically said, "I heard that!" then collapsed sideways onto the bench. Phillip also wanted to collapse, but wouldn't let himself until he had said what he wanted to say. He looked over at Foot just as he was pushing himself back up to rest on his right elbow. And simultaneously they both said, "Listen…"

"Me first!" Foot insisted. "I can't stay propped up like this for long."

"Sure," said Phillip. "Go ahead."

"Ok, here's the thing," Foot said weakly. "I'm feeling feverish."

"You want the blanket?" Phillip asked getting up.

"No!" protested Foot. "Sit down. What I'm telling you is that my leg is infected. I can even see a streak of red moving up. That means blood poisoning. So I'm not going to last a whole lot longer."

"No!" shouted Phillip. "Don't talk like that!"

"Listen to me!" Foot insisted. "What I'm saying is just the reality of the situation. So…if we don't sight a ship in the next day or so and I don't make it, I want you to know that, even though I may be tough as old leather, you would do me a great honor if you would use whatever's left of me to stay alive."

Phillip looked puzzled—then horrified. "You don't mean—" he started.

"I mean," Foot interjected, "that there's an unspoken agreement among seafarers that's as old as boats that says anything you do to preserve life is good and holy."

Phillip *was* horrified. "Foot," he said authoritatively, "I understand what you're saying, and I understand why you're saying it, and there's no doubt in my mind that you're right yet again—but I don't want to hear any more about it. OK?"

"Enough said," replied Foot as he lowered himself back down onto the bench.

"Not quite," insisted Phillip. "Not until I tell you that, well, I've had a lot of opportunity—and a lot of reasons—to do a lot of thinking the last few days, and…I want you to know that…well…I know it's not much and right now it seems so pitifully little that I'm embarrassed to say it but…please accept my apology."

"For what?" Foot asked.

"For being such a jerk," said Phillip looking away. "For prejudging you and not giving you the respect you deserve. For being arrogant and self-absorbed and ruthless and rude and insensitive and all the other fine qualities that I now know brought me to this point in my life. But what I really want to apologize for is dragging *you* into my mess. *You risked your life to save mine, and I wasn't even grateful.* And now…"

That's where Phillip broke down and could go no further. All he could do was to put his head in his hands and weep with profound, soul-shaking remorse. It was like all the stress and fear and exertion of the last few days was coming out at once in one great, cathartic flood. Foot reached out to try to comfort Phillip but he was too far away. "Don't," Foot said. "You'll dehydrate." But his voice was far too weak for Phillip to hear over his own lament.

Foot struggled to sit up, causing him to yelp with pain loudly enough to break into Phillip's misery. "What are you doing?" Phillip asked while moving to help Foot. "You should lie down and save your strength."

"Somebody's got to keep watch," Foot moaned as he achieved an upright position.

"What do you mean? For sharks?" Phillip asked.

"No," said Foot, "for ships. That storm drove us a long way south before it tried to tear us apart. We just might be close enough to spot something. It's worth keeping a lookout, anyway."

"You think so?" Phillip asked hopefully. "Then I'll do it. You lie back down and save your strength."

Phillip helped Foot lie back down, then moved up to the bow and painfully stood fully erect. He shaded his eyes with his hand and started scanning the horizon. There was enough of a breeze to fill the sail if they'd had one. There also a slight chop and it was all Phillip could do to keep his balance.

His muscles rebelled in pain and didn't want to respond to his commands to shift this way and that as the boat bounced gently up and down. So Phillip closed his eyes and took in a slow, deep breath as he had seen Foot do. "It's all about balance. It's all about balance," he repeated to himself. Then he slowly stretched out his hands and moved them in a wide circle as Foot had done. It hurt, but it was a good hurt, and it did make him feel more sure-footed.

While he stood there, eyes closed, the breeze cool against his burned face, he reflected on Foot's comment days earlier. *"You're like the surfer who thinks he can ride the waves without getting wet."* Then he remembered Foot describing himself as a life-surfer, and the full impact of the meaning hit him with such clarity. *It's thinking that you can navigate the seas of life without facing the tide of inevitable tests, challenges and the consequences of your actions*, Foot would like the reference to the sea, he thought. *It's about how those actions affect your character and integrity, your sense of purpose and ability to lead so that others will follow.* He knew what Foot meant now and hoped he would have the chance to tell him.

Phillip opened his eyes and started a slow scan of the horizon. The sun was higher overhead, and the heat waves coming off the water made the actual horizon somewhat blurry. Even so, Phillip could see that there was something not quite right about it. It was really more of a feeling than anything he could actually see, but there seemed to be a speck of something floating in the shimmering heat waves. Since there was nothing else to look at except the endless water, Phillip amused himself by watching the speck bob and float on the bending light rays, sometimes disappearing altogether, but always coming back to dance in the wavering ripples.

Phillip seemed to notice that the speck was growing larger and denser. Instead of riding on the shimmers, it seemed to be caught within them and distorted. His heart skipped a beat. Was he really seeing something or was this a mirage? He wasn't ready to say that he was really seeing something yet. The disappointment would be too crushing, yet he couldn't take his eyes off it.

Try as he might to keep his hopes down, the longer Phillip stared at the spot, the higher his hopes rose. He stared at it for what seemed like hours, several times switching the hand used to shade his eyes to avoid cramping. Though he never would be able to pinpoint the exact moment, somewhere in the process Phillip became aware that it *was* a ship—but he would not let himself say so until he was absolutely sure.

Then Phillip made out a shape—he thought—the silhouette of a ship. Then he could make out a bridge, then a smokestack. "Foot!" he screamed at the top of his lungs. "Foot! Foot!" He wanted to say, "A ship!" but couldn't form the words. All he could do was point and scream, "Foot! Foot!"

Foot heard the excited tone of Phillip's voice and sat up quickly. He did his best to stand and stared hard in the direction Phillip was pointing. And there it was. A ship. A cargo ship, by the look of her.

"We're saved!" screamed Phillip as soon as he could form words again. But Foot gently said, "Slow down, shipmate, we're not saved yet. She's much too far away for them to see us, and it looks like she's on a course that will take her no closer to us than a mile or so, still too far for them to see us."

Phillip's hopes fell as fast as they had risen. "You mean we've come this far only to have to watch her go by?" he asked sadly.

"Unless we can figure out some way to signal her," Foot said.

"Signal?" responded Phillip. "What sort of signal?"

"Like a smoke signal—if we had anything dry enough to burn, which we don't and something to light it with, which we also don't have," Foot said.

"This is torture!" Phillip moaned.

Then Foot suddenly looked wide awake and sharp as a tack. "Wait a minute!" he exclaimed. "Get me my uniform jacket from the forward compartment!"

Phillip had no idea what Foot could be thinking, but he quickly scrambled for the jacket. When he handed over the jacket, Foot went straight for the inside breast pocket and pulled out Phillip's solid gold, business card case.

"Remember this?" he said with a grin. "This useless thing you wanted to throw overboard? Well, watch this!"

Foot angled the case so that it caught the sun and its reflection could be clearly seen on the water. Then he directed the reflection toward the ship and passed it over her three times quickly, then three times slowly, then three times quickly again. He paused and did it again.

Over and over, Foot spelled out SOS in Morse code as the ship continued to sail. It was close enough now to see that she was a substantial cargo ship with cranes on the deck. It was as close as its path would pass them, but still there was no acknowledgment of their signal. The ship passed through its closest point and was now beginning to move away. Phillip felt his heart begin to sink.

Then, all of a sudden, there was a light blinking on the ship, a light that seemed to be aimed at them. "They've seen us!" Foot shouted. "They've seen us! Look! They're turning!"

And, so it was. The huge vessel was beginning to turn. Phillip almost swamped the boat getting to Foot and hugged him until Foot cried out in pain. Phillip laughed and cried and danced all at the same time. Foot smiled through his pain and kept signaling to guide the boat to them. Nothing in Phillip's life had ever taken as long as it took for the ship to reach them and haul them aboard using one of the cranes and a cargo net. Then everything went black.

Phillip woke up in bed in the ship's hospital ward, dressed in clean white shorts and a tee shirt, clean shaven—and starving. A smiling man sitting near the bed got up and said something in Spanish. Phillip gestured to his mouth and the man called someone on a phone. Minutes later, Phillip was amazed at how few tortillas stuffed with beans, potatoes, and chorizo it took to stuff him to the gills.

As he was finishing, the ship's doctor came in and asked, in thickly accented English, how Phillip was feeling. Phillip assured the doctor he felt fine, but the doctor checked him over anyway. When the doctor was finished, Phillip asked about Foot and the doctor took him next door to the surgical bay.

There, Phillip found Foot sitting up in bed with a mountain of food in front of him. As soon as Foot saw him, he sang out, "Ahoy there, shipmate! Come make a pig of yourself!"

"Already have," replied Phillip cheerfully. "How are you doing?"

"I'm doing splendidly," Foot reported. "The good doctor got my leg all tidied up and he's been pumping me full of antibiotics and taquitos like there is no tomorrow."

"How long have I been out?" Phillip asked.

"Two days," replied Foot. "The doc says I'll be up and around in one more."

Phillip bit his lip. "Yeah," he said. "Listen, Foot, I don't know how things will come out when I get back, but however it goes down, I'll keep my balance this time. I know I will. And wherever I land, there will be a place for you, if you want it."

"And give up surfing?" said Foot with a twinkle in his eye.

"Foot, how can I ever repay you? You lost your foot for me, *the one you were named after*, the one you put out in front when you surf. I feel horrible."

"Why?" asked Foot reproachfully. "You think this is the end of something? Well, let me tell you something, 'Every new beginning comes from some other beginning's end.'[8] Remember when I told you I must need a change? Well, while I've been lying here, I've been thinking maybe it is time for me to pursue a more lucrative profession, something that gives me more time to surf."

"Like what?" Phillip asked.

"Well," said Foot, "I've thought of writing about the sea. Some of my favorite authors are the ones who have inspirational tales to tell about courage and sacrifice and daring-do—and now, it just so happens that I have such a tale to tell, don't I? Just imagine me walking into a book signing with a peg leg and maybe an eye patch, telling a tale of seafaring peril and raw survival. I'd leave 'em breathless, I tell you!"

"I'm sure you would," said Phillip sincerely.

"Maybe I'll start a seafaring adventure for leaders where we strand 'em at sea with nothing but a few cans of peaches. How would that be?" Foot continued. "Or, maybe I'll design surfboards for the disabled and give lessons. I'm *swimming* in possibilities. Thanks for the offer, though."

Phillip just shook his head but not in disbelief. He was used to Foot surprising him. He was just reflecting on the fact that Foot had just lost his leg saving a jerk and yet here he was acting like he had just won the lottery.

For the next five days before the ship docked in Sydney, Phillip spent hours at Foot's bedside. They ate, slept, played chess, and talked late into the night like old war buddies. When they docked, saying goodbye was tough. "I feel like we've spent a lifetime together," said Phillip, "and I know I'm a better man for it, thanks to you. If you ever need anything, and I mean *anything...*"

"Here," Foot said as he handed Phillip the solid gold business card case. "I told you that you might feel differently about it one day." Phillip took the case with speechless gratitude. Then Foot gave Phillip a big bear hug and said with a smile, "Phillip, a new chapter of your life is being written right now. Write it well."

And with that, Phillip nodded, choked back his tears and left the bedside of the man to whom he owed his life.

Phillip walked just across the hallway, picked up the phone, and dialed his CEO. And he began telling the story, the whole story...and the whole truth.

Foot took a deep breath, leaned back on his pillow and that warm, familiar grin spread across his face.